Lifeguarding Simplified

THE MANAGEMENT PRINCIPLES AND TECHNIQUES OF LIFEGUARDING

LIFEGUARDING

By
Richard D. Baker

SIMPLIFIED

The Management Principles
and Techniques of Lifeguarding

South Brunswick and New York: A. S. Barnes and Co.
London: Thomas Yoseloff Ltd

A. S. Barnes and Co., Inc.
Cranbury, New Jersey 08512

Thomas Yoseloff Ltd
Magdalen House
136-148 Tooley Street
London SE1 2TT, England

Library of Congress Cataloging in Publication Data

Baker, Richard D. 1935-
  Lifeguarding simplified.

  Bibliography: p.
  Includes index.
  1. Life-saving—Training. 2. Life-saving—Management.
  I. Title.
GV837.15.B34   363.1'4   79-5386
ISBN 0-498-02482-2

Printed in the United States of America

This book is dedicated
to all lifeguards
who accept their responsibilities
with conviction and courage.

Contents

7

Acknowledgment

The author wishes to thank the American National Red Cross for access to the Longfellow Historical Archives.

Introduction

The job of lifeguarding, as we know it today, is an outgrowth of the lifesaving movement that began in the eighteenth century. During this movement three basic principles evolved, in the recreational and legal context of the times, which presently characterize the duties of an area offering lifeguard protection. By the proper application of these three simple principles a professional level lifeguard operation can be achieved at any water recreation area.

Basic Principles of Lifeguarding

1. The bathers and users of the protected beach or pool must be supervised.
2. The activities of the bathers and users of the protected beach or pool must be controlled.
3. Rescues must be properly made when necessary.

In chapter 1 this book offers some advice to the person looking for his or her first job as a lifeguard. Chapters 2, 3, and 4 discuss the three basic principles of lifeguarding and chapter 5 surveys the lifesaving movement that gave birth to these principles. A consideration of the lifesaving movement helps us to understand where we are today in lifesaving and lifeguarding. The final chapter of this book comments on organizational and administrative aspects of modern lifeguarding.

The words "lifesaver" and "lifeguard" were formerly written

either as "life saver" or "life-saver," and "life guard" or "life-guard." In this text the older spellings are followed when names or quotations make such usage necessary for accuracy. The hyphenated form is used once in the fifth chapter, although not historically necessary, in order to emphasize the difference between the "saving" and "guarding" aspects. Otherwise, the author's preference for the modern spelling is followed.

On May 5 and May 6, 1978, I instructed a nineteen hour course on the Management Principles and Techniques of Lifeguarding at the Marine Science Consortium, Wallops Island, Virginia. I organized this course under the sponsorship of the Marine Science Consortium. The Management Principles and Techniques of Lifeguarding course (MPTL) was structured from this book. Professionals in lifeguarding and aquatics attended the course and staff members of the American Red Cross and the YMCA were also included. Later that month, the American Red Cross at a national convention passed a resolution to develop and implement a lifeguard certification course.

A second MPTL course was held on May 30 and May 31, 1979 at Ocean Pines, Maryland. Ocean Pines has four community pools and is seven minutes from the large ocean resort of Ocean City, Maryland.

Future MPTL courses will be planned for various suitable localities, to meet the needs of both beginning and established professionals in aquatics. *Lifeguarding Simplified* will be the text for these courses.

Richard D. Baker
August 17, 1979

Key to Diagrams

∴∴∴∴   Beach

〰   Shoreline
‒ ‒ ‒   Sandbar

‿   Wave

⌣   Flat Wave

〜〜   Broken Wave

⇐ ‒ ‒   Direction of Water Movement

Diagrams by Hannelore Ingrid Bienia

13

Lifeguarding Simplified

THE MANAGEMENT PRINCIPLES AND TECHNIQUES OF LIFEGUARDING

1

A Lifeguard's First Job

Lifesaving involves the support of a victim in the water, transporting the victim to safety, the administration of artificial respiration if necessary, and some basic knowledge about personal safety in the water. Lifeguarding is all of this and more. It is a responsible forty hours or more per week job open to public scrutiny and subject to accountability.

Preliminary Training

Candidates for a lifeguard position should be certified in advanced lifesaving and standard first aid. The American National Red Cross teaches these courses to the public free. The successful completion of these courses, prior to working as a lifeguard, will make the training for lifeguarding and adaptability to the problems of lifeguarding much easier.

The candidate for a lifeguard position should follow a workout program prior to either employment or to a competitive examination for a job. Performance requirements will vary, depending on the organization. However, lifeguard candidates should at least swim one quarter mile with a sustained front crawl stroke regularly for two to three weeks before reporting for work or tryout. The candidate should also run a mile regularly for the same period of time.

For those candidates lacking in strength a minimum of two to three months of supervised weight training will build up shoulder, back, and leg strength. This strength is needed in carrying people through shallow water, and handling boats or paddleboards.

17

Attitude

The new lifeguard should arrive at the job ready to learn, willing to cooperate, and able to serve. There are many things about the lifeguard operation and the people to be guarded that a lifeguard will learn on the job, even though preliminary job training may have been very thorough. New lifeguards are usually the weakest link in an operation, and their immediate cooperation is important in order to balance their inexperience. Some new lifeguards are so impressed by their new position, or background, that they tend to forget that they were hired to serve. Few new lifeguards realize how crucial their attitude is to successful employment.

Stress

Lifeguarding is a job that often entails mental and physical stress. The conditions that produce stress may vary. Large crowds, severe weather, numerous rescues or near drownings, an uncooperative citizen—all tend to cause stress. Skills must be learned quickly in order to adapt and cope with these stresses.

The Sun

For outdoor lifeguarding a tan should be acquired, if possible, before reporting for work. Above all, avoid getting sunburned. Use sunscreens, or block outs when needed. Lifeguards should cover up when suitable, and watch their skin. A dermatologist should be seen if irregularities appear. Good body oils help reduce skin dryness.

New Responsibilities

Bathers and other users of the beach or pool with lifeguard protection must be supervised. Activities at the beach or pool must be controlled. Rescues must be properly made when necessary. These are the basic principles of lifeguarding. Techniques of supervision, methods of control, skill with rescue equipment, and

Lifeguards at Rehoboth Beach, Delaware do a morning workout. The lifeguard standing next to the stand holds a rescue tube, and a lifeguard to his right holds a surf buoy (Photograph by Author).

knowledge of the characteristics of rescue situations will enable a lifeguard to meet the new responsibilities of a first job.

Summary

A lifeguard should prepare for his or her first job. Do not get overcome by the new responsibilities because of inadequate preparation. But don't arrive on an ego trip either. Arrive prepared and ready to improve.

2
Supervision

"In twenty five years' study of water accidents, I found that the remedy for the average bathing accident to be plenty of public bathing places, properly supervised." [Commodore Wilbert E. Longfellow]

The key to supervision is observation. The purpose of observation is detection.

Five general situations require quick detection by the lifeguard. The lifeguard who is observing from a suitable position will be able to see what is happening by using a technique called scanning.

Need for Observation

1. The scanning lifeguard must constantly look from left to right, and occasionally look to the rear. This requires moving the head. A lifeguard who never moves his or her head is not scanning. The lifeguard only stops scanning when something has been spotted that needs further observation. In the diagram above there are examples of five general situations a lifeguard (#1) should spot quickly:

2. This nonswimmer is drowning. The victim is in a vertical position with his or her head partially submerged. Also, the victim's arm movement is not a swimming type stroke but an ineffective pushing down on the water.

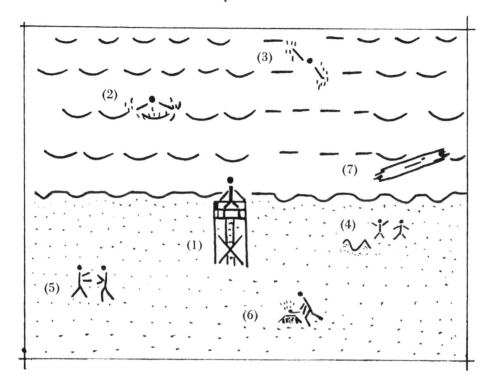

3. This swimmer is in distress. Although stroking vigorously for shore, the victim is trying to swim against a current and isn't making any progress. The victim realizes that there is a seaward current and instead of swimming out of it to the side has panicked. A rescue should be made before exhaustion overcomes this person and a drowning begins.

4. Two children are running down to the water leaving a big hole they have dug on the beach. They should be made to come back and fill it so no one will step into it accidentally and get hurt.

5. These two chaps have decided to have a brawl. They may hit someone else on a crowded beach before they are finished. They should be stopped.

6. With an offshore wind, the odor of the hamburger being cooked over this open fire might drift over to the lifeguard.

The fire should be put out and any coals removed before someone steps on them.

7.   This is a large board that has come in to shore because of a storm. It presents a very dangerous condition and should be removed; or people should be kept out of its path until it lands on the beach.

These above examples represent the following five general situations that a lifeguard should spot quickly:

Drowning...................................(#2)
Distress....................................(#3)
Dangerous conditions..................(#4, #6, #7)
Disorderly conduct.........................(#5)
Infractions of regulations...................(#6)

Both the case of the hole and the fire should be considered dangerous conditions and, if regulations exist for both, infractions

Head lifeguard Jack Gilliss supervises the beach from a stand at Assateague Island National Seashore (Photograph by Author).

of regulations. However, at many beaches people are allowed to dig holes and that in itself is not an infraction, although leaving it can be dangerous. Open fires are usually not allowed by order of the beach regulations.

Positions of observation

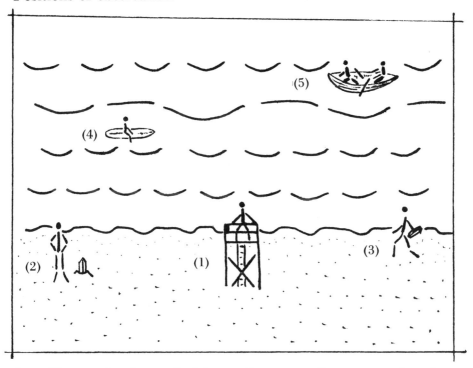

1. Observation from a height, such as a stand or tower, gives the lifeguard a good perspective.
2. By taking a position at a particular area on the beach the lifeguard can be on the spot at a hazardous area near shore.
3. This lifeguard takes a buoy along and conducts a walking patrol near the water's edge. The patrolling lifeguard's main concern is to be in a general area rather than at a particular spot.
4. This lifeguard sits on a paddleboard inside waves that break on a sandbar behind the guard. Sitting up on the board the lifeguard has good observation in this middle area and can respond quickly, maneuvering the board between swimmers if necessary.

This 1901 photograph shows two lifeguards supervising the beach at Asbury Park from a stand. The stand is placed in the middle of the life line area (Photograph courtesy of Library of Congress).

5. These lifeguards are outside the sandbar and, sitting on the boat's thwarts, have better visibility than a lifeguard who is on a board. This boat houses equipment such as: a ring buoy attached to a line, a torpedo buoy, a rescue tube, and a long pole that can be used for rescue.

Pointers on observation from the stand:

a   Learn to put on suntan lotion while watching the water.

b   Wear a good pair of sunglasses. The glare of the sun from the water can not only bother your eyes and give you a headache, but it impairs your ability to see well.

c   Do not get too comfortable. Stand up now and then or change your position. If you start to feel lazy, then you are not as alert as you should be.

d   Answer questions from the public courteously, but quickly and to the point. Only look at the questioner briefly. If someone speaks to you from the rear of the stand, ask the person to come to the side where you can both hear each other better, and you do not have to turn around to be heard.

e   Do not allow people into your stand to talk to you, take pictures, and more. They do not have your responsibilities and may lack good sense. They may also physically get in your way, block your vision, unintentionally kick equipment off the stand, and more.

f   Do not permit people to put up umbrellas that will block your view of the water. Make them move the umbrellas to the side and to the rear so that you can see the water at all times. A lifeguard's blocked vision is a hazard to safe water use.

g   When possible do not let people congregate or recline directly between you and the water.

h   Remember that some things that happen in the water start out on the dry beach. Troublemakers on the deck or berm can become troublemakers in the pool or surf. Know what is going on.

i   Communicate potential problems with other lifeguards. Good lifeguards work together as a team. Lifeguards not on a stand may look to you for directions because of your better observation from the stand.

j   Always have your equipment properly set up and ready

to go. If you have to look to get equipment that is not ready, you will probably regret it.

k   Every six or seven scans, look to your right and left, if there are stands there, and see what the other lifeguards are doing. Do not get lost in your own little world.

l   Watch the water as much as possible when you communicate with another lifeguard. Phones on stands with coiled, extension type lines, are the best stand to stand communication.

m   If you are on the stand with another lifeguard do not let a conversation interfere with your job.

n   Scanning from a stand is hard work except when no one is around. It often requires great concentration and can even give some lifeguards a headache by the end of the day. Workouts, eight hours of sun, scanning, and maybe a rescue or two, can add up to physical exhaustion by the end of some days. Be prepared to make the effort, because it is not a snap if you do it right.

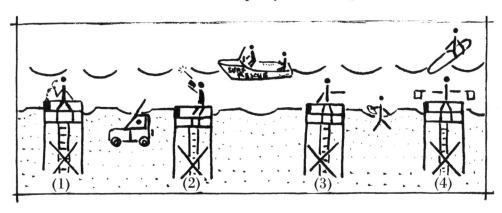

Communications

1.   This lifeguard can call by phone to another stand or off the beach to a supporting administrative unit. The cord is of sufficient length so that no observation is lost while conversing. The message is kept brief and official.

2.   The lifeguard in the stand is talking to the lifeguard in the beach vehicle. The message is also heard on the radio in the surf rescue patrol boat.

3.   The lifeguard in the stand has hand signaled a lifeguard on walking patrol to enforce a regulation.

4. The lifeguard on the stand signals with flags to the lifeguard on the paddleboard.

    Purpose of communications:

    a   Directions from a supervisory lifeguard
    b   Lifeguards seeking instructions or advice from a supervisory lifeguard
    c   Requests for aid in terms of people or materials
    d   Alerting to dangerous or unusual conditions
    e   Alerting to an action about to be taken
    f   Equipment handling responses
    g   Dispensing routine information

A lifeguard at Ocean City, Maryland uses semaphore to communicate with another lifeguard (Photograph by Author).

3
Control

"The use of surfboards and similar devices is prohibited within the limits of designated swimming beaches." [*Code of Federal Regulations, Title 36—Parks, Forests, and Memorials*, Section 2.28 Swimming and bathing, (e).]

Beaches and pools that are supervised by lifeguards usually will be subject to some regulations. Besides the responsibility of providing nonnegligent supervision most lifeguards also will be responsible for enforcing these regulations. Supervision, combined with regulations, zoning, and safety directions, are the elements that allow for control of activities and use.

Regulations

Pool Regulations

1. Soap shower required before entering pool area
2. No pets allowed
3. Alcoholic beverages prohibited
4. Glass bottles prohibited
5. Running or pushing on deck prohibited
6. No diving from shallow end
7. Safety directions of lifeguards must be obeyed

The above examples of regulations are typical for a pool. A soap shower is required for the same reasons that pets are not allowed

28

This surf bathing regulation sign is characteristic of the control that exists on
Australian surf beaches. Swimmers and surf bathers must only go in the water
between a set of red/yellow flags. These are set up to mark the safest area
(Photograph by Author).

—sanitation and health. Alcoholic beverages are prohibited at
some places to help preserve public order. The possibility of
broken glass, falls from running or pushing on deck, and hitting
the bottom by diving from the shallow end, obviously are significant because of the usually wet hard, deck and hard bottom that
are part of a pool's structure. Finally, it is necessary to give
authority to the lifeguard so the general intent of safety can be
followed without trying to cite and post every conceivable,
hazardous action.

Zoning

1. Dangerous or defective conditions

At the lake beach in this diagram a large rock not far from shore may be an invitation to the unaware swimmer to come and use it as a diving platform. However, two other rocks, not visible from the surface, stick up from the bottom in front of the unsubmerged rock. Consequently, a sign has been put up and the area marked off. This safety action is an example of controlling use at this beach through the creation of a restricted zone.

At this ocean beach a rip current area is flagged, and a sign prohibits swimming in this part of the beach. The current may be flowing only part of the day, depending on the height of the tide and the size of the waves. However, when the bottom changes and the current doesn't exist regularly on a daily basis, the flags and sign should be removed. Possibly a new area will need to be zoned.

Areas where swimming or bathing are not allowed can be regulated and controlled for the use of other suitable activities, as shown by this sign on Bondi
Beach, Sydney, Australia (Photograph by Author).

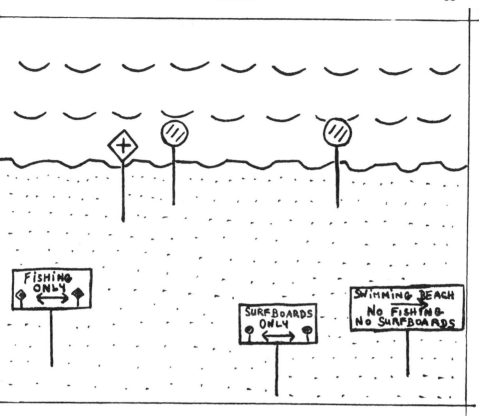

2. Activities

The diagram above illustrates how an ocean beach may be zoned by signs based on activities. Neither surfing nor fishing are safe activities in a swimming area because of the danger of injury to swimmers. On the other hand, surfers and fishermen often infringe on each other's activities if they are using the same area. Creating separate zones eliminates conflict.

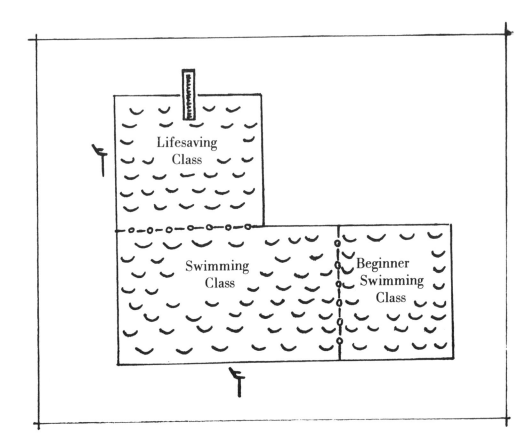

In Diagram H the L-shaped pool has been zoned for aquatic instruction. The zone areas have been created by lines and floats. The use of these zones will be controlled by the instructors who take their classes to the proper areas. The zones allow the beginner class to use shallow water, the swimmer class to use adequate swimming depth water, and the lifesaving class to use the deepest water.

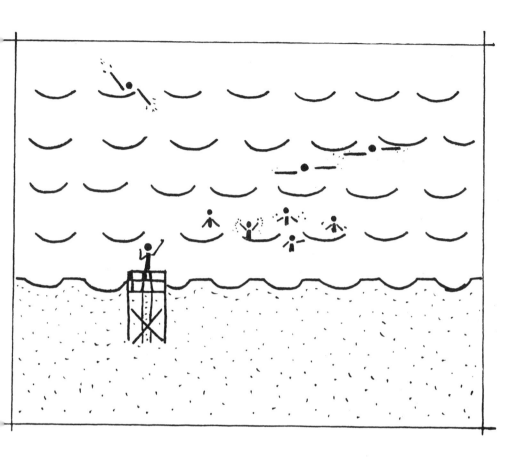

Safety Directions

The lifeguard in the above diagram signals to a swimmer who is heading out of sight but not out of mind, to stop and come back. Distance swimming at a protected beach should be alongshore, because lifeguards cannot adequately supervise swimmers who are far offshore.

A swimmer has just stepped onto a sandbar and proudly turns around to show everyone that he is in shallow water. The lifeguard motions him to come back to shore. Experience has shown this lifeguard that although a good swimmer can make it to the sandbar if this person is allowed to stay many poor and even non-swimmers will attempt to go to the sandbar. Consequently, the lifeguard should not allow people to swim to this sandbar until the bar has built in closer to shore and will be relatively safe. Preferably the lifeguard should stop the swimmer in deep water before the swimmer reaches the bar and can stand up. If this is done many people will not know a sandbar is there and will not try and get on it. Many safety directions such as this will be the result of experience with the people and the protected area.

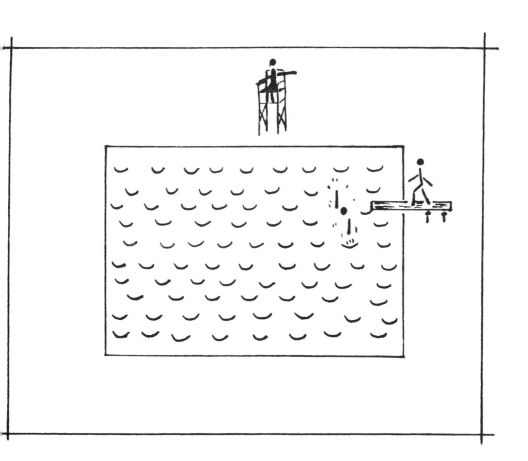

In this diagram the lifeguard at the pool stops the person on the diving board from diving until the swimmer in front of the board gets out of the way. At pools, children forget to exercise good judgment or even common sense. The lifeguard constantly must be alert under these circumstances in order to prevent serious injuries, including spinal injuries of the back and neck.

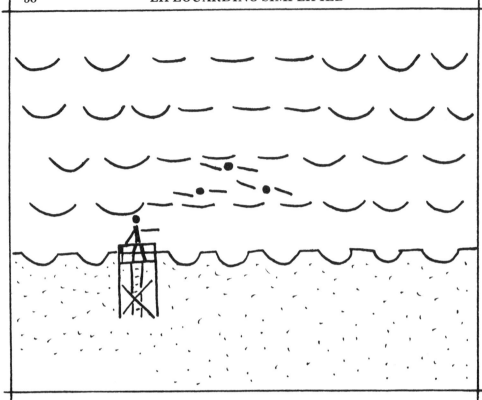

At the surf beach above three swimmers are in a dangerous current. The lifeguard directs them to swim to the right in order to get out of the current before they panic or need to be rescued. If this current persists, the area should be marked with flags and/or posted and closed to swimmers until it stops.

Manner of Enforcing and Directing

The enforcement of regulations and the issuance of safety directions sometimes can be matters of great aggravation to both the lifeguards and the public. This aggravation can be increased greatly if the lifeguards, through inexperience or lack of thought, handle the situations poorly. The following are some tips on how to handle enforcement and safety directions so the lifeguard is more effective and friction is minimal:

Lifeguard Tom Daisey informs two children about a regulation concerning the use of air mattresses as floats, at Chincoteague Protected Beach, Assateague Island National Seashore (Photograph by Author).

a   Always be courteous and businesslike
     Most people appreciate courtesy and respect a businesslike approach. On the other hand, the people you direct do not have to be courteous or polite to you. The question is, do they in fact comply with the directions? If properly approached or directed most people will immediately comply.
b   Be specific and clear as to what is wrong. Also be explicit as to what you want people to do.

Hand signals from the stand should be slow and precise. You can walk down a street and see people wearing glasses everywhere you look. How many people swim while wearing their glasses? You should take factors such as this into consideration.

Explain regulations or safety directions if you make a personal contact. Tell the person his or her alternatives if there are any.

c   Do not apologize when you enforce a rule or give a direction.

You will never convince the public that regulations and safety directions are beneficial if you apologize for doing your job. On the contrary, if anything, you should explain and justify the action.

d   Do not be a compulsive whistle blower.

One of the quickest ways for lifeguards to gain an image of incompetence in regard to control is to blow whistles constantly. Whistle blowing should be kept to a minimum. However, when it is blown it should produce the desired attention or make a personal contact, if a voice gun or public address system is not used. When practical, a personal contact is preferable to using a voice gun or public address system. An effective and quiet service is usually appreciated by the public.

e   Identify yourself by name and position when appropriate.

Whenever a situation of noncompliance seems to be arising, or when the violator for some reason may not know that you are a lifeguard, identify yourself by giving your name and your position. Make it clear to the violator that you are a lifeguard with proper authority at that area.

f   Do not argue with the violator about the basic facts of the situation.

Although it is appropriate to explain the violation, and the regulation or safety order, a lifeguard should not get involved in an argument about the basic facts of the situation. If the violator wants to argue it is usually best to contact your supervisor or even call another lifeguard. You may also find it advisable to have a lifeguard for a witness if the violator does not appear to be reasonable or rational.

g   Know where regulations are posted and know the source of your authority.

Some members of the public will state that they did not see any regulations posted. If they are correct then the regulations should be posted. Otherwise, you should know where the regulations are and be able to point this out. Also, you should be able to tell them the law that gives you the authority to take action.

h   When a violator with knowledge of your identity and of your legal request refuses to comply, then you should proceed calmly and cautiously. If informed of the alternatives, such as a violation notice, calling the police, or possibly an arrest, most noncompliant violators will change their minds. However, your actions up to this point should have been decorous, or such a person will complain of the way the situation was handled. If a supervisor is available, it is often best to call this person, both to be a witness and because the violator will often receive the attention he or she may have wanted and will then comply.

In cases of noncompliance clearly state the alternatives or consequences to the violator or get the help of a supervisor.

4
Rescues

"Drowning is an unlovely thing." [Commodore Wilbert E. Longfellow]

Support of Victim

Most rescue equipment can be used to support the victim. An exception to this is reaching extensions such as: poles, shepherds crooks, and heaving lines. The degree of support necessary will vary with the situation. Obviously, the more flotation the equipment itself has, the better support it will be able to give the victim. Flotation possibilities will range from minimal, with a ring buoy, to the substantial flotation of an 11' or 12' rescueboard, and the adequacy of a boat.

The ability to maintain support will also vary depending on the conditions, the equipment, and the victim. Large or chop waves may threaten stability on a rescueboard or even in a boat. A slim victim may be easier to handle and balance than someone obese. A rescue tube can be secured around a victim in a way not possible with a torpedo buoy.

Transportation of Victim

Rescue equipment is important in the transporation of the victim from deep water and danger to safety. Equipment can increase the safety of both the victim and the lifeguard and can increase the speed of the transfer. Safety is enhanced with equipment because of the flotation support, added freedom of movement for the lifeguard, and because bodily contact with the victim can be either minimized or conducted within a basically controlled procedure. Speed is possible because of both the increased flotation and propellent possibilities. In the case of a line brought to the victim, speed is increased because the lifeguards on shore can easily pull in the line once the victim is secured.

Recovery of Victim

When a victim has sunk, it may be necessary to use equipment to facilitate the finding and recovery of the body. Consequently, skin or scuba diving equipment can be essential. Masks, snorkels, and fins are basic for this work; and wet suits may be necessary if cold water is a problem.

Adaptability to Situation

Equipment is necessary in order to adapt to the needs of the victim and the environmental situation. With an assortment of available equipment the element of choice is present and this gives the lifeguard a chance to respond more effectively to a variety of circumstances.

Maintaining Control

It is possible to maintain control of the area if rescue equipment is used. The lifeguard who uses a shepherd's crook at a pool can maintain better observation and control of the pool than the one who unnecessarily jumps into the water and makes a swimming rescue. At a beach a lifeguard who uses a rescueboard, if the circumstances are favorable, is at an advantage in comparison to swimming out with no equipment. For example, by sitting up on the board the lifeguard has good observation of the area and can be seen better by swimmers if the lifeguard wishes to give directions.

Extension Equipment

1. Poles

    The simplest type of water rescue is a situation where the lifeguard, without going into deep water, reaches out and grabs the victim by the wrist and pulls him to safety. Rigid poles that extend beyond this reach are the simplest type of equipment. However, in such situations one may also use the shepherd's crook that can encircle the body.

2. Lines

    It is possible to extend lines to the victim over a much greater distance than it is possible to extend a rigid support. A heaving line can be thrown by using the weight of part of the line while it is coiled. This is the simplest type of line extension. By attaching one end of the line onto a ring buoy the buoy can be thrown and the line can be extended farther and with greater accuracy.

    Lines that are not thrown to the victim are carried to him, usually by a swimming lifeguard, although they can be brought out by lifeguards in a boat or on a rescueboard. In this manner lines can be brought out over hundreds of feet of water. In using the line in this way it is usual for the lifeguard, upon reaching the victim, to get behind him and securely to support him. The line may be brought initially out attached to a torpedo buoy, to a rescue tube, or to a belt attached to the lifeguard. Consequently, in some cases additional equipment will be present to aid in support. Once the victim is secured the lifeguard with the victim will signal to the other lifeguards on shore and the line will be hauled in.

    Because lines that are brought out to the victim are usually quite long, in the vicinity of 600' or more, it is necessary to keep them ready so they will not snarl and tangle. They may be kept ready for use by coiling them carefully in a tub, or by coiling them on a reel. Most commonly they are coiled on reels, and the equipment is then known as a "line and reel." The main advantage of the reel over the tub is that it is quicker for recoiling the line. The tub, however, is probably less subject to line entanglements.

Ocean City, New Jersey lifeguards move their surf boat closer to the water line
as they begin the day's operation (Photograph by Author).

Mobile Floating Equipment

1. Boats
    There is a significant variety in the type of boats used for
lifeguarding. The choices include: the three thwart, the flat
bottomed rowboat, the Cape Cod dory, the five man surf
boats, the motor driven boats, and even the catamaran.
    The use of boats offers the lifeguard various methods for
contacting, supporting, and rescuing the victim.

a   The boat is maneuvered for close contact with the victim.

b   The boat is kept away from close contact with the victim, and equipment in the boat is extended or thrown to the victim.

c   The boat is kept away from close contact with the victim, and a lifeguard leaves the boat to rescue the victim.

Great care must be used when rescuing with a boat to avoid collision with the victim or contact with the propeller on a motor boat. A lifeguard who leaves a boat to make a rescue should both leave and reenter the boat on the directions of the operator or the lifeguard in charge. The operator or lifeguard in charge is responsible for the safe handling of the boat.

Boats have an advantage over other types of equipment when long distance rescues or when a long patrol on the outside zone is needed. They lose this advantage with short distance rescues and when rescues are needed in crowded areas. They also are excellent for a relatively fixed patrol area on the outside of rafts or floats.

Lifeguards who use boats should be trained to get experience in the following four phases:

1   the launch
2   the approach
3   the rescue
4   the return

Three factors will complicate these four phases:

a   water conditions
b   wind and weather conditions
c   the presence of people in the water

2. Paddleboards (Rescueboards)

Paddleboards have evolved from the surfboard. The present surfboard is too small to be considered a satisfactory rescueboard, although it can serve as a means of support for a victim. However, it lacks the transportation characteristics and the stability of a rescueboard. A good rescueboard will support and transport an adult victim and an adult rescuer both prone on the board with the board maintaining stability (evenness) and freeboard space between the board and water, at the bow. The author prefers nothing less than an 11' rescueboard with preference for 12' (although 14' is not too long). With boards shorter than 11' there is a tendency for the rescuer to have to be too far to the rear in order to trim the board so that about 3" of freeboard is under the bow. Without this freeboard in ocean surf conditions, the bow could submerge and cause the board to "pearl," or dive under and then flip. However, on calmer waters such as small lakes, the longer length of the board would not be quite as critical.

Generally, the advantage of a good rescueboard may be compared to boats in the following ways:

a   Only one lifeguard is needed to use a board.
b   Boards can be quickly moved laterally along the shore so they can be launched opposite the victim.
c   They can usually be launched more quickly than boats.
d   In the water the board is more maneuverable than a boat under most conditions.
e   The board is safer to use in a heavily used area.

Rescues with boards must be done in close contact with the victim, and the methods for contacting and supporting the victim are more limited than with a boat. The following contact and support procedures are generally used:

1   The victim or victims simply grab the board for support.
2   The victim is slipped on the board in a prone position.
3   The lifeguard first flips the board over. Then by holding the victim to the board, or by the victim holding on himself, the board is again flipped and the victim is rolled onto the board.

As with boats, lifeguards who use a rescueboard should be trained in the following four phases:

a   the launch
b   the approach
c   the rescue
d   the return

These phases will also be complicated by the factors of:

1   water conditions
2   wind and weather conditions
3   the presence of people in the water

Frequent use of the board during in-service training is necessary for those lifeguards who have not handled a board previously. In this way they may learn balance and stability on the board.

3.   Buoys
       The limitation of the throwing ring buoy, in regard to flotation, has been pointed out. The larger ring buoys that are aboard ships or on docks are used mainly by dropping over the side of the ship or dock near the victim who, with this larger buoy, can use it for significant support.
       The other type of rescue buoy that is widely used is the buoy that is towed to a victim by a swimmer. There are various shaped buoys used in this manner such as the diamond shaped buoy. The most common and popular buoys are the torpedo buoy, and the rescue tube. The torpedo buoy has a towing line that should be approximately 3 1/2′-4′ long, and a halter that by slipping it over a shoulder makes it possible to tow the buoy in the water. There are either grab lines around the buoy or molded hand grips that can be held by the victim or used by the lifeguard to hold the victim to the buoy. On one end, the buoy should have a small loop of rope or molded gap on the shoreward end of the buoy while it is being towed out. To this rope, molded gap, or other fixture, it is possible to hook or attach a line that can be extended out to the victim with the buoy and then hauled back to shore.

Although numerous lifeguard organizations have used metal torpedo buoys for many years, it is not the best type of material considering safety. A metal buoy can cause injury if for some reason, usually a wave or carelessness, it violently contacts the victim or rescuer. Obviously, the most likely area of contact would be the head. The same objection may also be made in regard to fiberglassed buoys, and for any buoy with projecting metal eyelets.
However, lightweight and extremely durable torpedo buoys

A pair of diamond shaped buoys are set up on a special stand for a quick pick-up in Ocean City, New Jersey. Diamond shaped buoys are common along the protected beaches of New Jersey coast (Photograph by Author).

have now been made from plastic materials presently available through modern technology. These buoys are not as dangerous as the metal buoys, yet, they provide excellent buoyancy and are well designed to support and transport victims.

Chas. D. Corey DBA of Huntington, New York makes an excellent torpedo buoy, internally composed of expanded polystyrene and externally covered with nylon reinforced vinyl plastic. This buoy has four grab lines, one on each side of the buoy, and the 30" long buoy has a weight of only seventeen ounces with a buoyancy of twenty-one pounds. The 36" long buoy weighs twenty ounces and has a buoyancy of twenty-five pounds.

For rescue situations involving multiple victims, Marine Rescue Products of Newport, Rhode Island distributes a buoy from Surf-Saving International that is called a "rescue can," which is made of crosslinked polyethylene. This buoy has molded hand grips and a hookup gap for a line formed of the polyethylene material. Although harder and heavier than the Corey buoy, the "rescue can" is not dangerous in the manner of the metal "can" or torpedo buoy and does not have any dangerous projecting metal eyelets as some fiberglass buoys do. The #200 can by Surf-Saving International is 34" in length and weighs five pounds.

The torpedo buoy cannot be bent around a victim like a rescue tube can because of the torpedo buoy's rigidity. But the torpedo buoy can be tied around a victim by using the tow line in an emergency situation that requires such an action.

Advantages of the torpedo buoy include:

a   the grab lines or hand grips facilitate group support

b   by grabbing lines or the grips, rather than grabbing the larger body of the buoy, the victim tends to remain lower in the water and is often more stable and more effectively towed back to shore

c   the grab lines, more so than hand grips, are helpful to the lifeguard for holding the buoy to the victim

d   the rigidity of the buoy makes it easy to set it up on beaches for quick pickups

e   a shorter lead line is possible on a torpedo buoy as compared to a rescue tube

Rescue tubes are buoys that usually have a halter and a tow line similar to a torpedo buoy; but the tubes are flexible and there are no grab lines. A metal snap will be at the opposite end to where the halter is attached. The rescue tube will be slimmer than most torpedo buoys and the rescue tube tow line will be longer than 4'. This is advisable because when the tube is bent the tow line attaches to it at a place close to the victim's body. With a torpedo buoy in a tow situation part of the buoy itself extends the distance between the rescuer and the victim. The problems with long tow lines—the author prefers a tow line of no more than 4' on a torpedo buoy—should be kept in mind when using a rescue tube since:

1   With a tow line longer than 4' there is a good possibility that many lifeguards will step into the loop of the hanging rope when they run with the equipment, if they carry the device waist high.

A lifeguard off 12th Street at Ocean City, Maryland in 1978 tows a woman on an air mattress to safety, using his torpedo buoy (Photograph by Author).

2   A longer tow line will have more of a tendency to go slack in the water. This can interfere with the leg kick, and it can cause lost time while the rescuer tries to find the sagging line to present the buoy to a victim.

The primary advantages of the rescue tube as compared to the torpedo buoy are the following:

a   The tube can be bent around the victim. When the tube is bent and snapped, it is relatively secured. For towing purposes, the tube part should usually be around the victim's chest and the snapped part behind the victim's back. For support of a nonbreathing victim so that artificial respiration can be facilitated the tube part should be around the back of the victim and the snapped part should be to the front.

b   The tube can be bent around the lifeguard. If the tube is bent around the lifeguard with the snapped part at the lifeguard's back, this will facilitate keeping the lifeguard in a high position to give artificial respiration.

Making Rescues

Australian beach inspectors successfully revive a drowning victim at Bondi Beach. The mechanical resuscitator has already been used, and the victim is now in a face down position to prevent aspiration of stomach fluids (Photograph by Author).

A rescue occurs when a person who was either in distress or drowning is supported and then transported to safety. In rescue situations where breathing has stopped restoration of breathing by artificial respiration takes precedence over transportation, if it can be done effectively.

RESCUE CASE NUMBER V-72-9, ASSATEAGUE ISLAND NATIONAL SEASHORE.

The day was August 26, 1972. The time was 3:30 P.M. Low tide would be at 4:08 P.M. Waves were breaking on the sandbar with a height of 1'-2'. The littoral (alongshore) current was right to left at a velocity of about (.5) M.P.H. The protected beach had four lifeguard stands on it, numbered 1 to 4 from left to right. Six lifeguards were on duty. At 3:30 P.M., four lifeguards were in the stands. One was just completing a daily 1/4 mile afternoon swim and the other lifeguard had just started his 1/4 mile swim. They were swimming with the current, right to left.

A couple in their mid-twenties were enjoying themselves in a liferaft just to the right of the protected area near stand #4. They drifted over into the protected area with the littoral current where the raft was not allowed. The lifeguard in stand #4 stood up to direct them to move south, out of the protected area. The liferaft was just inside the sandbar. Suddenly, a wave hit the raft and knocked the couple out of it. They were then separated from their raft, and eighty yards from shore. They tried to get on the sandbar and the male started to make it, as the waves brought the raft toward shore. The young woman could not get up on the bar because of the wave break and the aerated water. That was not her only problem. She also could not swim.

The lifeguard in stand #4 immediately went out with a torpedo buoy. The lifeguard in stand #3 had observed the incident and noticed that now both people were in deep water, the male returning because of the plight of his companion. He picked up the phone on his stand, dialed stand #2 and said, "cover." He then picked up a buoy, ran opposite stand #4 and swam out.

When the lifeguard from #3 reached the area the male was near the raft and the woman was supported with the buoy by the lifeguard from #4. The male was told to get on the raft and bring it to shore after he stated that he was fine. The lifeguard who was supporting the woman was behind her, with his arms under her arms, and holding her to the buoy that was in front of her.

The victim was not a large woman and probably did not weigh over 120 pounds. But she was terrified and irrational. A torpedo buoy can support three or four people who are rational and will follow the lifeguard's directions. A buoy will not support the same number if they are irrational and try to climb up on the buoy, using their strength to depress it and consequently creating a wavering and unbalanced flotation device. In spite of being securely held by a 190 pound lifeguard, this woman was depressing the buoy and generally creating havoc during the lifeguard's attempt to bring her to shore.

The lifeguard from #3 left the male after he got on the raft and swam over to the other victim. He gave his buoy to the lifeguard and told him to use both of them in supporting the woman and he would swim in towing them. The woman depressed both buoys and continually gave the lifeguard from #4 problems in keeping her controlled. Nevertheless, they began to bring her in to shore.

When lifeguard #3 had called lifeguard #2 and told her to cover,

Lifeguard stands and lifeguard office at Chincoteague Beach, Assategue Island National Seashore, 1974 (Photograph by Author).

she immediately came down to stand #3. When the other lifeguards took their afternoon swims, they made a habit of glancing
up at the stands. Both swimming lifeguards saw #2 lifeguard leave
her stand and pick up a buoy and both left the water at that time.

The lifeguard who had just started his swim was nearest to the
rescue. He ran to stand #4 and, snapping the line from a line and
reel around his chest, swam out. The other lifeguard ran to stand
#4, just behind him, and began to handle the reel, playing out the
line and keeping it from tangling.

When the hookup was made with the line the victim was about
thirty-five yards offshore. After the hookup, lifeguard #3, who
had been towing, went closer to the victim to help the other
lifeguard. At this point the woman let go of the buoy she was
holding and grabbed #3 around the neck. Her reaction was still
irrational; after grabbing #3 around the neck she thrust her own
head backward and began to submerge it in the water. Lifeguard
#3 grabbed the line that was being towed in with one hand and put
his other arm behind her neck. He had to use most of his strength
to bend her head toward him and keep it out of the water while
maintaining his hold on the line with the other hand. Soon, they
were in the shallow water and it was all over. After she was carried
to the beach the victim was quiet and not at all irrational.

This rescue incident is an example of how a rescue situation can
occur unexpectedly, develop complications, and be handled
efficiently and effectively by a well trained lifeguard crew. A 1'-2'
wave break is not big and not necessarily a hazard to a liferaft. A
120-pound woman who uses all her strength to offset efforts to
save her is not your typical rescue victim. The swimming lifeguards who maintained an alertness, even during their afternoon
training swim, quickly appraised the situation while running to
the vicinity of the rescue and responded by bringing out another
piece of equipment to facilitate the safe transport of the victim.

Lifeguards must be ready for the unexpected. Lifeguards who
take a 1/4 mile afternoon swim should be able to come
immediately out of the water, run 1/4 mile, and swim out and
make a rescue. Lifeguards must be able to analyze the problems in
a rescue situation. And lifeguards must understand the function of
equipment so they can use it effectively. In the above rescue the
only direction given was when lifeguard #3 told #4 to take the
second buoy and control the woman with both buoys while they
were towed in to shore. Other than that there wasn't an exchange

of directions or signals other than the signal to tow in the hooked up line.

A line and reel rescue is made at Bondi Beach by beach inspectors and some volunteer lifesavers, including the young boy at the right who was first to get to the reel to keep the line from tangling as an inspector went out with the line (Photograph by Author).

RESCUE CASE NUMBERS V-75-1, V-75-2, ASSATEAGUE ISLAND NATIONAL SEASHORE.

It was June 14, 1975. The time was 4:20 P.M. Low tide would be at 7:12 P.M. The wave height was 3' and breaking on the sandbar. Only two stands were in operation with three lifeguards on duty. In stand #1, on the left, there were two lifeguards. In stand

#2, on the right or to the south, there was one lifeguard.

Someone came running up to stand #1 and told the lifeguards that north of the protected beach, about 200 yards from the protected boundary, a man had been trying to get on the sandbar and could not seem to make it. This person had already been noticed by the lifeguards, but no sign of trouble had been apparent from this distance. One of the lifeguards immediately jumped off of the stand, saying he would check it out, picked up a buoy and ran north. The other lifeguard picked up his phone and called stand #2 and informed that lifeguard of the situation. This lifeguard informed the lifeguard in #1, that two lifeguards, not yet employed, were on the beach in his area, and if something developed he would try and get them to help.

The lifeguard in #1 looked at the problem area with binoculars. He saw the lifeguard swimming out toward the three people in the water. One of the lifeguards on watch had started to walk north on the beach. The lifeguard in #1 indicated to her by a hand signal that she should go where the incident was. She immediately began to run but she did not pick up a buoy.

One of the three people started to come toward shore. As the swimming lifeguard reached the remaining two people, the lifeguard and these two started moving out suddenly, passing over the sandbar. The lifeguard in #1 knew that this vicinity occasionally had either an offshore or rip current. All three were obviously in a rip. They were now about 100 yards offshore.

The lifeguard at #1 called #2, who saw what was happening, and asked him if he could handle the protected area by himself while #1 took off to help. Lifeguard #2, said "yes," and added that the other lifeguard on watch had just come over, and he was sending him to #1 stand. The lifeguard in #1 hung up the phone, grabbed a buoy and ran north.

Upon reaching the beach opposite where the people were offshore, the lifeguard from #1 found the unemployed female lifeguard and a man from another agency, who was watching with binoculars. The lifeguard asked for the binoculars. He could not see any indication that the heads were coming toward shore.

About half way to the sandbar they met a young man swimming in who said that the people out there needed help. They continued swimming in the general direction of the rescue scene but could not see anybody because of the size of the waves. Finally, after getting out over the sandbar, they heard a call for help to their left, and quickly swam over to the three people who were there.

The first lifeguard had both arms under a middle aged man and was holding him to his buoy that was next to the man's chest and was supporting his head to keep it out of the water. The victim was unconscious and did not appear to be buoyant at all. A young man was in front of the unconscious man, also holding onto the buoy. He and the other young man who had come in had supported the unconscious victim until the lifeguard had reached them. The young man was exhausted.

The lifeguard just arriving with the second buoy took off the halter and gave it to the female lifeguard and told her to tow the exhausted young man in to shore. As soon as she started in she then went over to the other lifeguard and changed places with him. After changing places he told him to take the halter and tow rope of the buoy and tie it around the victim. When this was done both lifeguards pushed the buoy around the victim so that it was behind his back where it could keep his head out of the water. Then they both grabbed a line on the buoy and began to stroke in with him, using a shallow arm pull.

As they started to swim, now about 150 yards offshore, they headed diagonally to the north. This was a maneuver to get them out of the rip and back to the sandbar. They made good progress and eventually reached a point on the sandbar where they thought they could touch bottom and keep their heads above water. Here, one of the lifeguards tried to do mouth-nose resuscitation. He could not force any air into the victim so they then proceeded to come straight in, having gotten out of the rip current.

When the second lifeguard from #1 took off, with the lifeguard on watch coming over to take the stand, the lifeguard in #2 picked up the phone and called the district office, a building behind the dunes and about 1/4 mile south. Asking for the district ranger, he told him that he needed transportation immediately to take either a line and reel or a paddleboard to the north of the protected beach. The district ranger told him to pick up a board and meet him at the vehicle crossover onto the beach just north of the protected boundary.

The lifeguard at #2 quickly called the unemployed lifeguard at #1 and told him to close the beach if he could not handle the protection himself, and then picked up a board and ran north. He reached the crossover just as the district ranger arrived with his

Lifeguards at Atlantic City, New Jersey make a rescue using boats. The life-guard in the stern of the boat to the left has thrown a ring buoy attached to a line to the victim. The victim was drawn to the boat and then brought aboard (Photograph by Author).

truck. He threw the board in the back and they raced up the beach.

The two lifeguards with the unconscious victim were met half way in from the sandbar by the lifeguard with the board. The other victim was being brought into shore about this time by the female lifeguard. The unconscious victim weighed well over 200 pounds and, not being buoyant, was not easy to handle. The buoy around his back had to be untied and thrown out of the way. The man was then placed on the board, face down. Then with one lifeguard paddling on the board the other two stayed on the sides and continued to stroke and make sure the victim did not start to slide off.

Upon reaching shallow water the victim was put in a three man carry and the lifeguards ran out of the water with him. They were now nearly 300 yards north of the protected beach. A spine board was on the beach and a resuscitator was ready, all taken from the ranger's truck. Another ranger met the lifeguards informing them that two doctors were ready to work on the man. The lifeguards put the man on the board and the two doctors began CPR. One of the lifeguards went to the head of the victim and held his head for the mouth-to-mouth resuscitation. The doctor couldn't get any air in and began to orally aspirate the victim. After a few minutes, the doctors advised that they could do no more for the man and that he should be taken to the local doctor in town. Two lifeguards and a ranger got in the back of the truck with the victim, maintaining attempts at CPR. The other lifeguard went back to the protected beach to resume duty at a stand. In town the man was pronounced dead by the doctor.

In contrast to the first rescue case presented here this second case was one in which discussion and communication was needed. Communication from the protected area and backup capabilities by a knowledgeable ranger staff were also important aspects of the second case. More of a problem in the second case than in the first was maintaining adequate protection while getting involved in a rescue since it brought lifeguards 200-300 yards outside the protected beach.

An obvious difference in the cases is the condition of the victims. The victim in the first case was buoyant enough to stay up until the lifeguard reached her with a buoy. However, she did not know how to swim and was terrified and acted irrationally, creating a problem. The exhausted, young man in the second case quietly complied with directions and wasn't a problem. The unconscious victim who was not very buoyant, was heavy, and had what appeared to be a completely obstructed airway, making attempts to revive him ineffective.

RESCUE CASE NUMBERS M-72-1, M-72-2, M-72-3, M-72-4, M-72-5, ASSATEAGUE ISLAND NATIONAL SEASHORE

The day was June 25, 1972. Five young people ages seventeen, nineteen, twenty, twenty-two, and twenty-three were on the beach again. They made the same request to the head lifeguard that they had made several times before. They wanted to go out to the sand-

Young volunteer lifesavers make a rescue at Tamarama, Sydney, Australia. The volunteers here wear yellow and red caps, except for the young lad to the left. The rescuer had control of the victim from the rear, and is just about to release him in shallow water (Photograph by Author).

bar. The head lifeguard had previously refused this request. Today he did not.

All five were students from Australia. One of them had been a member of the Surf Life Saving Association of Australia and had done duty at Manly. They were used to big surf. Very few other people were on the beach at this time. So the head lifeguard told them that today they could go to the sandbar for a while.

The time was 3:45 P.M. Low tide had been at 1:00 P.M. The waves were 3' high and breaking on the bar about forty yards offshore. The bar had a crescentic shape, and where it came in closer to shore on the left, the waves suddenly started to break very nicely left to right. This current met a right to left current from about 100 yards away from the other side of the crescent. The currents met and flowed together outward over the bar. A rip current had formed and the five Australians were in it.

All five people began moving out unable to come in against the current. Four lifeguards were on duty on a three-stand beach. The head lifeguard immediately went out with a paddleboard. He quickly put three of the victims on the board. Two other lifeguards came out with buoys. One of these buoys was attached to a line and reel. The other two victims not on the board were towed in with the line by the lifeguard who stayed inshore. The lifeguard with the unattached buoy started to ferry in one of the victims from the board. The former member of the Surf Life Saving Association of Australia had developed a severe cramp in his calf and could not kick. He had grabbed the line, and all five were quickly brought in to shore.

Supervisory lifeguards have to use their judgment in controlling beach use. When a decision is made and trouble follows there isn't any substitute for being prepared with suitable equipment so people in trouble can be brought to safety.

RESCUE CASE NUMBERS M-73-21, M-73-22, M-73-23, ASSATEAGUE ISLAND NATIONAL SEASHORE.

On August 27, 1973 the wave height was only one foot. The time was 12:30 P.M. Low tide would be at 1:36 P.M. A lifeguard was coming into the shore from the sandbar completing a workout near the north boundary of the protected beach.

Three children, ages seven, nine, and ten, who had been playing in shallow water decided to go swimming in deeper water. They immediately got into an offset, a current moving seaward at an angle to the beach, but not straight out. The lifeguard coming in from the bar saw the children moving seaward. He also noticed a woman standing on the shore and watching them anxiously. She was the mother of two of the children.

The lifeguard swam to the children. At this point they were about twenty-five yards offshore. He immediately put one of the children into a cross chest carry using his right arm. With his right hand he grabbed the upper right arm of a second child who was on her back. The third child was trying to swim to shore with a front crawl, but was making no progress. With his left hand the lifeguard gave this child a hard shove in the back that moved the child forward a few feet. Then, alternately stroking with the left hand and pushing the swimming child the lifeguard quickly brought all three children into water shallow enough so he could stand up and carry them to shore.

On surf beaches most rescues without equipment should be in circumstances such as the above, mainly, when a lifeguard is working out. Circumstances on a surf beach are often too varied to go in without equipment unless a lifeguard has no other choice.

When there aren't any waves or no currents and the distance you have to transport a victim is short, just a few feet, there may be circumstances when you will not choose to use equipment. However, keep in mind that, unless you can keep that victim's face above water, you may not get back with a conscious person.

The purpose of making a rescue is not to show that you are a tiger. You want to be able to do more than retrieve bodies. You want to bring people back alive, if possible. It pays, therefore, to work with your brains as well as your body.

Follow-Up After the Rescue

1. Full Supervision and Control Restored

    As soon as possible after a rescue full supervision and control should be restored. Lifeguards who were involved in the rescue should resume supervision of the area after other necessary follow-up procedures have been accomplished. In view of the rescue or rescues it may be necessary to initiate different control measures.

2. First Aid Treatment of Victims

    A lifeguard or another qualified person should see to it that all victims who need first aid treatment get it and those who may need medical help should be able to see a doctor. Qualified lifeguards will have basic knowledge about the dangers of shock and the problems arising from the ingestion of water and the complications when either salt or fresh water gets into the lungs.

To facilitate obtaining proper medical help or first aid, emergency information should be available, such as the phone numbers of doctors, ambulance services, and rescue squads. Procedures for handling transportation problems should be known to all the lifeguards and other members of the organization who might be involved.

3.   Record of the Rescue

An organization that works in a professional manner will have its lifeguards obtain some information about the rescue. The rescue report is a document relating the organization of the lifeguards and their ability to meet their responsibilities.

Rescue reports will vary in type and design. Some may be cards, others sheets of paper. Key words may already be on the report so the lifeguard only needs to underline or circle certain responses. Whatever the design of the report, the following information is relevant to a complete report:

a   Who
      Who was rescued and who was the rescuer? Because some people will simply fade into the crowd or walk off without giving their name, age, and address, these particular people will have to simply be "unknown," with an approximate age.
b   Why
      Why was the rescue necessary? Identify the cause and the hazard.
c   Where
      Where did it happen? In what area was the rescue and how far out?
d.   When
      When did it happen? Month, day, year, hour, and approximate minutes.
e   What
      What was done to make the rescue? Equipment used— type of carry, and more. Also, if applicable, what were the weather and general water conditions for the day?
Because of the time element it is important to design rescue

reports to be filled in quickly. To this end, and for clarification, it is best to avoid narrative reports. Once the name, age, and address of the victim have been obtained, usually many victims or friends of the victims will be able to fill in these parts of the report themselves, and the time is put on the report plus the lifeguard's name, the rest of the report probably could be finished at the end of the day if necessary.

Completed rescue reports should be filed. At the end of the season these reports can be examined and analyzed. This analysis will be able to show the type of rescue problems that the lifeguard organization faces and because the basis for the analysis is documented, the analysis can be a persuasive argument for organizational needs. In case a complaint should be brought against the organization in regard to a rescue situation, the record of the case can always be retrieved for reference.

Rescue Hazards

1. Currents

    The fact that a dangerous shore current was running in the last rescue incident when the wave size was small, should not be a surprise to lifeguards although it probably is surprising to the average person. Currents are caused by a disequilibrium in the surf zone. At low tide, the topography of the beach has more of an effect on wave movement and breaks. Consequently, a variance in wave breaks is often caused near low tide even with small waves.

    The variance in wave breaks and sideways wave movement causes disequilibrium. This lack of equalness, in water height and current flow, tends to follow a pattern. This pattern is caused by the shape of the bottom.

    The shape of the bottom is disclosed by the way waves peak, break, bend, move sideways, or slow down. Therefore, by knowing the shape of the bottom and the pattern of wave movement, most currents in the surf zone are predictable.

    A minority of dangerous shore currents cannot be predicted or specifically expected. This is because of the variety of the approaching waves. Waves from different areas of the ocean may phase into each other trough to trough and crest to crest, causing large waves. They may phase trough to crest and crest to trough, causing small waves. Some waves will come to shore moving faster than other waves that are coming in at the same time. They may come in at different angles, crossing each other, and otherwise cause various short time break patterns. However, currents caused by irregular variances are seldom of any extended length and usually end quickly.

The causes or reasons for surf zone currents should not be confused with the currents caused by either an incoming or outgoing tide. Tidal currents may be caused near surf zones when large volumes of water are forced to move thorugh restricted areas such as inlets or alongside bay mouths. Most United States beaches have a tidal range between 2'-6'. The tide takes about six hours to rise or fall this distance. This will not cause surf zone currents in itself.

The main factors about currents that are important to rescues are the current direction and its length or terminal relationship to the surf zone. Current velocity variance

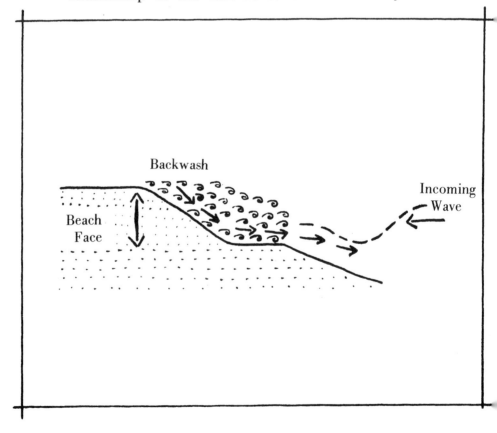

should not change the basic procedures for making a swimming rescue. Currents should be named so these important factors are understood. Labelling most currents as "rips" has done little more for our understanding than the old term "undertow" did. Only currents going through sandbars should be called rips. Nothing should be called undertow.

Current Types

1. Backwash

Backwash is caused by waves receding down a beach face and by seaward movement in the trough behind the broken wave crest. Obviously, the steeper the gradient of the beach face, the greater the possibility of strong backwash. Also, backwash is most likely at high tide. A person moved seaward, who cannot swim nor float, is likely to sink as he or she is moved into deep water. Such an occurrence may have led

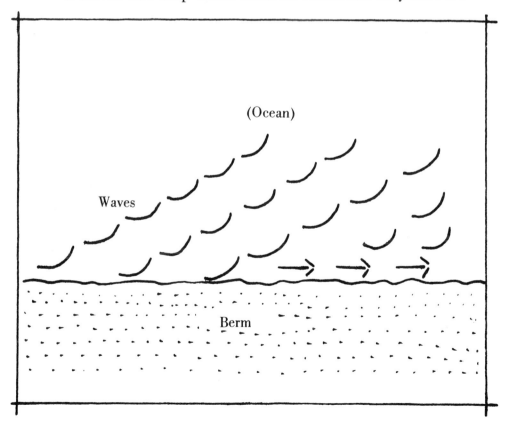

to the term "undertow." However, floaters or swimmers need not fear going under when in a backwash current.

This current moves directly seaward. It terminates when the next wave crest peaks and starts to break. Variance in wave heights can create stronger or weaker swashes, the water surging up the beach face after a wave breaks, and stronger or weaker backwashes in the receding water. Consequently, after being moved seaward by a backwash, the next wave crest may bring the person back in to the initial position if it is big, or leave the person further out than the initial position, if it is small.

2.   Littoral Current

Littoral currents are commonly caused by the direction that waves approach the shoreline. If waves come from the left, as in the diagram, they will first start to break with the part of the wave nearest shore, the left side. This break will move to the right as the right side of the wave gets into shallow water. This left to right break will release water in

The waves are coming toward shore from the north-east in this picture of Ocean City, Maryland. A strong north to south or left to right littoral current is created along the shore by this wave action (Photograph by Author).

that direction, causing a current flow.

The littoral current moves parallel to shore. It terminates when conditions change, such that waves do not come in the same, or the topography is different, a jetty obstructs it, and more. Backwash can take you into a littoral current. Littoral currents are the primary cause of the rest of the currents to be discussed.

Current movement in rivers is similar in many respects to littoral currents in the ocean. River currents sometimes directly parallel the shore. They meander with loops in the river. Ocean littoral shore currents are also changed by a "meandering" shoreline or sandbar contour.

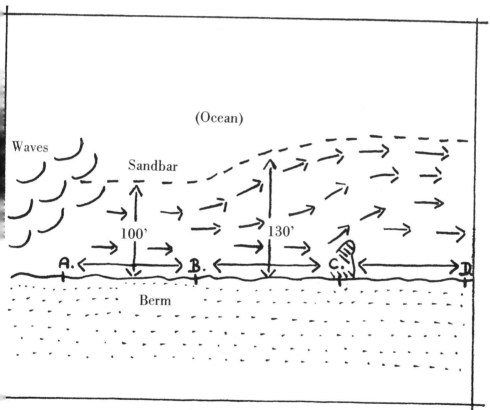

3.   Offset

An offset current is a littoral that diverges from shore, going seaward at an angle less than 90° and staying inside the contour of a sandbar. In the above diagram, area A-B has a left to right littoral current. The sandbar offshore at this area is parallel to shore. From B-C, the sandbar contour moves out and deep water exists 100' from shore where, to the left, a sandbar began. The littoral current disperses as it moves into the wider area of the surf zone.

The seaward dispersal or angleation of a littoral current creates an offset. The offset could also be caused by a sand deposit or other obstruction on the shoreline, such as at C. The offset terminates when an area of parallel contours is reached, such as at D.

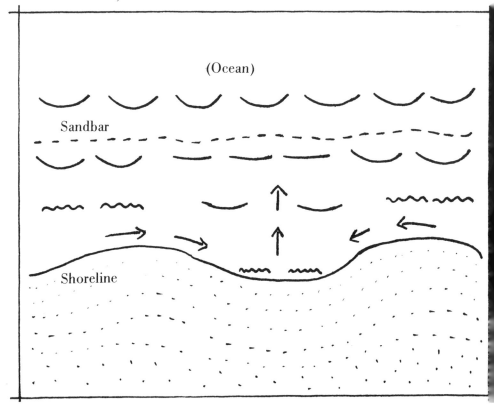

4. Offshore current

The offshore current goes directly seaward similar to a backwash current, but it is not terminated by an incoming wave crest. This current is caused by littoral currents meeting, and except for its termination inside the sandbar, it is a current very similar to a rip current. However, the fact that this current may bring a person close to a sandbar eventually, and not into just deep water, is quite significant. On the other hand, if it terminates before reaching the sandbar, a person may, of course, still be in deep water, although under either situation one will not have been brought out beyond the surf zone as one would have been by a rip current.

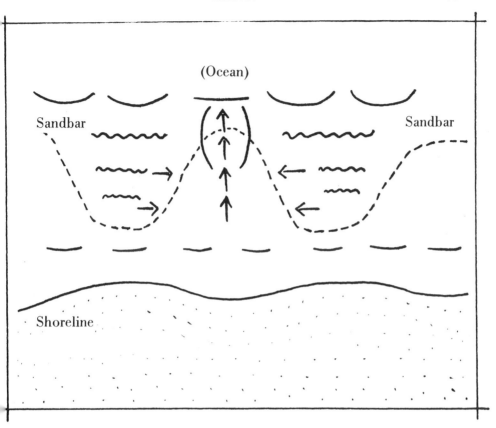

5. Rip current

The rip current cuts or rips, topographically speaking, through a sandbar. The critical topographic rip area in the sandbar (   ) will usually be 2′-3′ deeper than the adjacent sides, though not always. The rip current terminates outside the sandbar beyond the main wave break area on the bar. Consequently, it terminates outside the immediate surf zone. It is this characteristic that makes the rip current more dangerous than the other currents.

Usually, a rip current area is characterized by a greater variance in sandbar formation than that which characterizes the other dangerous shore currents. Because of this greater variance and because of the force with which this current moves, a rip current is often easier to spot than an offshore current, which may be less forceful and occur under less noticeable circumstances.

A lifeguard making a rescue should be able to swim directly to shore if the current is a backwash, littoral, or offset. However, if difficulty is encountered, the lifeguard

In this photograph, an offshore current area is easily seen. To the sides of it, the sandbar is very shallow. Most seaward currents will not be as obvious as this one, which is on Santa Rosa Island, Florida (Photograph by Author).

should angle for shore in the direction of the littoral current. If a swimming return is necessary in either an offshore current or a rip current, the lifeguard should swim directly to the side to the right or left, and come straight in after getting out of the current, or angle for the side while swimming in.

Waves

Swimming rescuers should either duck or dive under large, breaking waves in order to avoid the force of the waves. This force can move the rescuer toward shore or separate a rescuer from a victim. Aerated water, caused by breaking waves, can prompt a momentary loss of buoyancy. The rescuer should be prepared for this loss of buoyancy, especially when in the area of a large, breaking wave in relatively deep water. The rescuer should take a deep breath of air before going under the wave and may wish to wait until air bubbles in the aerated water dissipate somewhat before coming to the surface.

When waves are creating an active surf the swimming rescuer may have to grab the sand bottom with both hands, hold position while the surge from the wave passes, and then vigorously pull forward before going to the surface. Without fins, this may be the only way that a swimming rescuer can move out through a large surf.

Boats and paddleboards should be launched perpendicular to wave crests. The launch should be in the wave trough after a wave breaks and, perferably with large waves, when a relatively small wave is following. Boats and paddleboards can maintain a controlled position much better after launching if they are kept perpendicular to breaking waves. It is critical to maintain control of boats and boards in active surf.

Cold Water

Water that is at the temperature of about 60° Fahrenheit (about 16° Celsius) or less can be considered cold water for swimming rescues. A boat or paddleboard, if suitable for the rescue problem, is obviously a better choice than a swimming rescue in cold water. However, lifeguards who train every day will be helped greatly by this, in adjusting to rescue work in cold water.

5

The Lifesaving Movement

> "If you want to save a life you can join our corps. We will train you afterward. The impulse to save life is the thing we are looking for. We would prefer you to be a swimmer, but if you are not and want to be, you can belong. America needs life savers." [Attributed to life-saving promoter Col. J. Wesley Jones, in the radio play, "Guardians of the Beach," a history of lifesaving in America by Wilbert E. Longfellow.]

The lifeguard job of today was developed during the lifesaving movement and was shaped by it. Improved methods of life-saving have made possible a greater effectiveness in life-guarding. Changes in the public participation in bathing and swimming activities and legal actions through the courts in cases of negligence in regard to lifeguard protection, have altered lifeguarding methods and have helped to define standards. Consequently, a brief survey of the lifesaving movement will help to put a perspective on lifeguarding as it is today.

The Early Days

The lifesaving movement may be said to have started in 1767 with the formation in the Netherlands of the Maatschappij tot Redding van Drenkelingen. The records of this society, which was concerned with the restoration to life of those apparently drowned, were translated into English in 1773. Some men in England, headed by Dr. Hawes and Dr. Cogan, subsequently

74

organized the Royal Humane Society in 1774. In 1785, the life-saving movement became established in America with the formation of the Massachusetts Humane Society.

During the nineteenth century, both in England and the United States, most of the concern of lifesaving societies was with shipwreck and other nonrecreation related drowning situations. The National Institution for the Preservation of Life from Ship-wreck was founded in London in 1824. This later became the Royal National Life Boat Institution in 1854. Primarily using life-boats, by 1975 this organization had saved over 90,000 lives in the coastal waters off Great Britain and Ireland. But it was not until 1891 that an organization was started with the best methods of making swimming rescues as its primary concern. In that year the Royal Life Saving Society was formed. The methods developed by this society influenced, to some degree, the development of technique in Australia, South Africa, Germany, and the United States.

The lifesaving movement in the United States during the nine-teenth century was more complicated than in England. The federal government officially became involved in lifesaving when the Revenue Marine Division was ordered in 1831 to aid seafarers and ships in distress, and later in 1836, to aid those who could be taken aboard. A second line of development occurred a few years later because officials of the federal government had been favorably impressed by the work of the Massachusetts Humane Society. This society had set up unmanned lifeboat stations and small huts for use by survivors of shipwrecks at selected beach areas. The idea of establishing stations with lifesaving equipment for use by volunteer rescuers was adopted by the federal govern-ment, and in 1848 Congress authorized the spending of $10,000 for lifesaving on the dangerous New Jersey coast.

Boathouses with a surfboat, line throwing mortar, metal life car, and other marine supplies were set up by Captain D. Ottinger of the Revenue Marine Division. Later, money was appropriated for developing stations at other areas along our coasts and the Great Lakes. From 1854 through 1871, Congress authorized a system of paid keepers at the boathouses who were helped by volunteers. This system was unsatisfactory and it foreshadowed the general results of future attempts to develop a broad, volunteer system of lifesaving in the United States.

In 1871, Sumner I. Kimball was appointed chief of the Revenue Cutter Service and the Lifesaving Service was organized as a part of that bureau. Kimball rebuilt boathouses, obtained good crews on salary, and initiated the beach patrol that was maintained in darkness and bad weather. In 1878, the Lifesaving Service was made a separate entity under the Treasury Department and called the U.S. Lifesaving Service. This Service built an enviable reputation and was the subject of much praise in newspapers and periodicals. The Revenue Cutter Service and the Lighthouse Service were both joined with the U.S. Lifesaving Service in 1915 to form the present U.S. Coast Guard.

Apart from developments in government service, the United States Volunteer Life Saving Corps was founded in 1870 by Edwin D. Ayres. This predates the Royal Life Saving Society by twenty-one years. The lifesaving techniques of the U.S.V.L.S.C. primarily involved nonswimming rescues at this date. Later, methods for the swimming rescue would be adopted by this organization. These methods would come from former Royal Life Saving Society members to a man named Wilbert Edmund Longfellow, who would become a member of the U.S.V.L.S.C., and after modifying the English methods, he would eventually make them the skills and techniques of his own organization.

The Longfellow Era

Within the history of the United States Volunteer Life Saving Corps may be found a bridge of transition from the early days of unskilled swimming rescues, when reliance was mainly on boats, to the modern days of the skilled swimming rescue. The engineer who built that bridge was Wilbert Edmund Longfellow. By about 1898, Bert Longfellow became interested in lifesaving while working as a newspaper reporter in Rhode Island. He developed lifesaving techniques through contacts with former members of the Royal Life Saving Society, joined the U.S Volunteer Life Saving Corps, became head of the organization in Rhode Island, and started a one man campaign to reduce drownings in that state.

Longfellow achieved significant success in his attempts to reduce drownings. He lectured, demonstrated at beaches, and had equipment such as ring buoys placed on wharves. He also used his skills and contacts as a reporter to great advantage by managing to get appropriations for equipment from the state legislature and by writing to educate the public about safe and unsafe behavior in the water.

In 1909 he went to New York City to accept the top position of Commodore of the United States Volunteer Life Saving Corps. The corps had received state articles of incorporation from New York in 1890, and New York City was headquarters for the corps and its area of chief activity. Longfellow developed contacts there with Y.M.C.A.s, the newly founded Boy Scouts, the National Camp Director's Association, and the "National Recreation Association" (Playground Association of America). The lifesaving movement started to develop a broad base that hitherto had been missing in the country.

In 1914 Longfellow went to work for the American Red Cross. Shortly before this time he had made a break with the U.S.V.L.S.C. The Commodore had wanted to create a national program of lifesaving, through the U.S.V.L.S.C., but the Board of Governors of the organization did not agree with him. Fortunately, an opportunity to create a national program with the American Red Cross propitiously followed his resignation in New York. Officials of the Y.M.C.A. and the Boy Scouts had convinced officials of the American Red Cross that their organization should undertake the task of reducing drownings in the country. The Red Cross was willing, if the right man could be found to lead such a program, and all concerned agreed that Longfellow was the one for the job.

As Commodore in New York City, Longfellow had developed lifesaving methods to a standard acceptable to the organizations that contacted him for help. It was also in New York that he developed policies for training members of his own association, utilizing the public baths of New York City for this purpose. These methods and policies he continued after he joined the Red Cross.

As Commodore for the U.S.V.L.S.C., Longfellow had basically worked in New York City, but when he joined the Red Cross he became a national field agent. He started his trips in 1914 by going to Baltimore for two months, and then continued on to Philadelphia, Utica, Chesapeake Beach in Maryland, camps on the Delaware River, Atlantic City, Providence, Detroit, Cleveland, and New York City. During 1914 work was also done with the U.S. Navy at League Island and Newport.

In 1915 he made the first of his southern trips. However, when eight hundred people drowned from the disaster of the Steamer Eastland in the Chicago River, during this year, the field trip to begin the water safety program in the Middle West was made. Longfellow conducted a West Coast tour in 1916, and by the end of 1916 he had toured most of the important cities.

The Commodore had primarily gone to cities where there were drowning problems. There were also Y.M.C.A.s, police, and firemen, as a basis for starting a program. Waterfronts and wharves were target areas, such as in Baltimore, because these were extremely hazardous places with no protection and no equipment for rescues. Ocean front beaches were protected perhaps (in Atlantic City, a lifeguard was employed at the Seaview Excursion House in 1872, and a city lifeguard force was started in 1892— many other "watering places" had lifeguard services by 1880), but although there were "comparatively few drownings" at the ocean areas, "Bustem and Rollem," as Longfellow called them, were the lifeguards.

As he had used the public baths in New York City for training purposes while stationed there, the Commodore used the swimming pools of the Y.M.C.A.s around the country when he went on his field trips. Many of the early local Red Cross Life Saving Corps had Y.M.C.A. staff members, and many Y.M.C.A.s served as a local corps headquarters.

It was the Red Cross Local Life Saving Corps that Longfellow concentratred on organizing from 1914 to about 1920. His field trips stirred up interest in lifesaving and this interest led to applications for charters from the Red Cross. The local corps had authority when engaged to raise money for buildings and equipment. In the absence of widely developed Red Cross Chapters at this time, a situation changing with the war effort, the corps made volunteer service in lifesaving possible.

One of the earliest Volunteer Life Saving Corps, and one that has the distinction of still being in existence, was that of Jacksonville, Florida. Mr. H. W. Walters, and other members of the corps, developed the now famous, metal "can" torpedo buoy that became standard equipment at most beaches and pools for many years. This buoy was intended for use, when appropriate, with a line and reel, and had a buoyancy that could support up to five people.

Prior to joining the Red Cross, Longfellow had made a tour of girl's camps in Maine, in 1913. During this tour he had organized the World's Lifesaving Alliance for Women. This organization was the nucleus for the Red Cross Women's Corps in 1920, that allowed women to become part of Red Cross lifesaving.

Longfellow did not find his lifesaving candidates among the amateur swimming clubs in the country, unlike the English who got considerable support from these clubs. The Commodore found the amateur swim clubs in the United States "not interested," and he turned instead to those whom he called that, "vast body of underpriviliged swimmers," for his lifesaving candidates. Under Longfellow's leadership, the American Red Cross was the "Greatest Mother," and he began, as in Rhode Island, to thoroughly utilize the media and communications to accomplish a task of water safety education.

The faculty at the American Red Cross Life Saving Institute at Seaside, Oregon during June 1925 were, left to right, L. E. Palmer, Assistant Director Ed Carroll, Director Longfellow, Mille Schloth, and Paul Huedepohl (Photograph courtesy of the American Red Cross).

He used pageants to educate large crowds while he entertained them. "The Sea Rider" was a pageant that showed the public how rescues could be made from boats or paddleboards and warned people of the danger they faced if they did not "learn the ways of the sea." Talks were given to groups and over the radio, with the Commodore telling people about such things as "Coming Clean from the Fourth of July." Plays were also put on for the radio audience. Attention-getting epitaphs and slogans were created by Longfellow to make a point about water safety.

"Beneath This Stone Lies Henry B. Clyve,
Who Broke His Neck In A Shallow Dive."

"This Gravel's Reserved For Sylvanus Slack,
Who Swum To The Middle And Didn't Come Back."

Drowning and other statistical data was used by Longfellow. Films and stereopticon slides were part of his teaching program when a suitable water place was not available. Field contacts were succeeded by mail. Later, Longfellow wrote articles for: *Red Cross Courier*, *The American Swimmer Magazine*, *The Boy's Life Magazine*, *The American Girl Magazine*, and other periodicals as publicity.

The Commodore believed that many drownings were caused by the "he-man impulse." He utilized this factor to get these same people, males of ages 18-30, to show off their water skills by learning lifesaving. The Greatest Mother turned her drowning delinquents into living lifesavers. Longfellow also had much concern for keeping up the interest of lifesaving members, and gave advice to the local corps on how to keep a year around program going in order to hold interest and retain skills and "watermanship," through games such as water polo, through demonstrations, and with lifesaving competitions.

Longfellow was a charismatic figure. On his field trips he effected everyone with his enthusiasm, knowledge, and showmanship, but when he left many people lost much of their heartiness. World War I interrupted Life Saving Corps development too, but it also sparked the growth of more local chapters and this was in large part needed to support the promotional field work that Longfellow and, after the war, other field agents carried out.

Although Life Saving Corps organizations had some setbacks,

Longfellow was quite successful in getting large scale recognition throughout the country for the Red Cross lifesaving standards. As more private and public operators of pools and beaches began to hire lifeguards it became apparent in many places that the Red Cross certificate in lifesaving was necessary, not only in order to obtain competent lifeguards but to gain public confidence in the lifeguards.

The need for a steady, local organization that could support a continuing, community lifesaving effort was allied to the need for plenty of public swimming facilities where people could both learn to swim and swim under lifeguard supervision. Longfellow considered the years 1921-1927 as years the Red Cross made great strides in this area.

Also important to the movement during these years was Longfellow's initiation of the first "Learn to Swim" campaign in 1921, and the first Life Saving Institute, later called Aquatic School, held at Plymouth, Massachusetts in 1922. This institute was created to meet the problems of the New England summer camps. This was also a time when the Red Cross made important changes to the swimming rescue by placing greater emphasis on the proper approach to a victim and less emphasis on breaking away from the victim. The fear of "death grips" was giving way to a more positive attitude along with the continuing development of swimming rescue knowledge and technique.

With a base of local Red Cross Chapters, public facilities, and a proven program to offer the years 1928-1934 were ones Longfellow saw characterized by training people for aquatic leadership. From 1935 onward, Longfellow saw the Red Cross moving into the period of Education for the Aquatic Era, a program of mass education to be sustained of course by the leadership base developed in 1928-1934 and by future leaders.

Three major trends in lifesaving may be noted during the Longfellow Era with the Red Cross:

1. From a one man operation to greater organization and support within the Red Cross for the Life Saving Corps
2. From the acceptance of volunteer, local Red Cross Life Saving Corps as lifeguards, to the almost universal hiring of lifeguards with increasing demands from the public and local governmental authorities that they be Red Cross trained

3. From primarily providing service through the local Life
    Saving Corps, to teaching everyone to swim and providing
    education in water safety.

Lifesavers at Seaside, Oregon prepare to use a metal torpedo buoy with a line
attached during the 1925 Life Saving Institute. Commodore Longfellow
directs the proceedings (Photograph courtesy of the American Red Cross).

It is apparent from Longfellow's organizational and field work,
writings, and concepts and visions, that he was an intelligent man.
His brilliance enabled him to lead this country's lifesaving
movement with marvelous assurance during the most critical
stages of its development. He also had an intense interest and love
for his work. Finally, his sense of humor is obvious in much that
he wrote. Longfellow, affectionately known as the Amiable
Whale, was big enough for the job that he set out to do in more
ways than one.

Hawaiian lifeguards practice the Schafer prone pressure method of artificial respiration in 1920 under the watchful eyes of the Amiable Whale. During this Hawaiian trip, Longfellow became aware of the lifesaving capabilities of the surfboard, and he subsequently introduced this equipment at the Red Cross Life Saving Institutes (Photograph courtesy of the American Red Cross).

T. W. Sheffield

Although Captain Sheffield did not become a national figure comparable to Commodore Longfellow, his work in lifesaving was significant, particularly on the West Coast. He also had consider-able knowledge of rescue problems along the California beaches. Sheffield came from England where, as a young man, he became interested in lifesaving while working as a marine engineer. Like

Longfellow, his life spanned that period between crude and modern swimming rescue methods.

While in England Captain Sheffield trained in lifesaving under the direction of William Henry, who was the founder of the Swimmer's Life Saving Society later to be called The Royal Life Saving Society. Consequently, Sheffield came to the United States with a good background in lifesaving and, in 1915, he met Longfellow. This meeting was the beginning of a long affiliation with the American Red Cross. He also held a position as a Field Director of Water First Aid, as the lifesaving service of the Red Cross was then called.

Captain Sheffield was critical of California lifeguard services. In 1907 he noted that the lifeguard service in Atlantic City was far superior to the work being done on the Pacific Coast. Like Longfellow, he denounced the common belief among lifeguards that the correct procedure for overcoming a struggling victim was the knock out blow. Also, he was critical of the lack of knowledge in regard to proper resuscitation.

Simply, lifesaving qualifications were not being demanded of lifeguards on the West Coast when Sheffield became involved, although many lifeguards were good swimmers. However, few of them knew the prone pressure method of resuscitation, the method then considered the best, and few had even enough basic knowledge to know the necessity of immediately beginning resuscitation. Captain Sheffield became involved in trying to improve the lifeguard services at various California coastal cities through the organization and training of Life Saving Corps, and he worked hard to get the Red Cross lifesaving certificate accepted as a job requirement for lifeguards, whether they worked at a beach or pool. Particularly he was active at Santa Monica where the lifeguards he organized and supervised were about to take out a charter when the United States entered World War I, breaking up this potential group. During this conflict, Sheffield was involved in training servicemen in lifesaving as preparation for their combat duties.

During the late 1930s and early 1940s Captain Sheffield wrote some excellent articles for the magazine *Beach & Pool*. His series of articles on the "Evolution of Life Saving Services and Equipment" is an historical portrait of change during his life. "The Surfboard As A Medium Of Sport And Lifesaving" and "Points for Consideration In Beach Developments" were two articles he

This 1911 photograph of the beach at Venice, California shows the life line, so familiar at ocean beaches then, extending from the berm out into the surf. Most of the surf "bathing" was done close to these lines (Photograph courtesy of the Library of Congress).

wrote that were valuable contributions to the understanding of some of the problems and characteristics of ocean beach life-saving.

The Surf Life Saving Association of Australia

The Surf Bather's Association of New South Wales was formed in 1907 in Sydney, Australia, and from this came the existing Surf Life Saving Association of Australia. The forerunner to this national organization had been the Bondi Surf Bather's Life Saving Club that originated in 1906 in order to reduce the loss of life in surf bathing. Other club formations followed the Bondi organization and these clubs subsequently associated in the national organization.

The story of the lifesaving development in Australia is concerned primarily with surf bathing. In turn, the development of surf bathing, as an accepted public recreation in Australia, unfolds within a controversial context of private, public, and local governmental, moral, and recreational interests. The people of Sydney indulged in some surf bathing during the nineteenth century. However, there were restrictions on the hours bathing was permissible plus a constant concern by some people that bathers were not suitably costumed. The neck to knee costume was most consistently demanded by those afraid of a lack of decency at the beach. This amount of bathing apparel was still a matter of enforced law well into the twentieth century. The restrictions on bathing in the ocean during proscribed daylight hours was disobeyed by Joseph Gocher in 1902 who, although arrested apparently was not prosecuted, and from that time on sea bathing during the day was permitted although the law against it was not repealed.

The surf beach areas around Sydney eventually became public property. As early as 1864, the Waverly Council requested the Government to place a reserve at Bronte for public recreation, including sea bathing under the Council's control. This request was granted and in 1881 the Municipal Council took over the Bondi Beach area for public recreation. Later the Council constructed public baths and dressing sheds for the public, and also provided some lifesaving equipment. For example, in 1886 the Waverly Municipal Council purchased six throwable life buoys that were considered by the Royal Humane Society of Australasia as "the most suitable life-saving appliances for sea bathers." In 1902 the disappearance of life buoys and lines at Bondi Beach was brought to the attention of the Council, and in 1903 two life buoys were obtained by the Council for use at Bondi and one for use at Bronte.

The uneven and unsatisfactory state of lifesaving in Australia began to change with the growth of the surf clubs and the Surf Life Saving Association. The first carnival, a competitive demonstration of lifesaving skills, was held in February 1908, by the

Bondi Surf Bather's Life Saving Club, with other clubs participating. The purpose of the carnival was to raise money for life saving equipment. The surf clubs primarily used two kinds of equipment, surf boats and the line and reel.

The reliance on boats and the line and reel facilitated the type of cooperative team effort that has characterized much of Australian lifesaving and has been very influential throughout the world. This teamwork also adds interest to the carnivals the Australians so skillfully present. The equipment itself is indicative of a response to the surf conditions of the Australian bathing beaches and, to some extent, as a response to the shark problem before the netting of the beaches was successfully accomplished.

The surf conditions and public use patterns initially made it desirable to have moveable life lines. The reels, of course, are principally of value in keeping a line coiled and unsnarled and ready for transport wherever it is needed on the beach. Not being attached out in the water to a pole or anchor, but being attached to the swimming rescuer, the line can be pulled in when the lifeguard secures the victim. The boats allow a team to get out through big surf and protect the rescuer and the rescued victim from shark attack.

Australian lifesaving, particularly the use of the line and reel, has influenced many places including: South Africa, India, the Far East, and the Middle East. Their system of controlling bathing and swimming so that it is only allowed "between the flags" (areas where dangerous currents are minimal or absent), the placement of lines and reels at strategic locations, and the patrol outside the surf zone in boats, all result in an effective and efficient operation. The Australians have very successfully combined voluntary lifeguarding with the use of professional lifeguards. The Australian position of "beach inspector," a professional lifeguard, was created when the State of New South Wales passed the Local Government Acts of 1919. These professionals guard the beaches during the weekdays and direct the numerous volunteers who help them on the weekends and holidays.

The Deutsche Lebens-Rettungs-Gesellschaft

The motivation for creating the German Life-Saving-Society or DLRG, the most outstanding European lifesaving society, stems

The beautiful Australian coastline at Sydney has many bay beaches. In this 1971 photograph, Bronte is to the left and Tamarama is to the right (Photograph by Author).

from an accident in 1912 in Binz on the Island Ruegen on the Baltic Sea when a pier collapsed, sixty people fell into the water, and seventeen of them drowned. When the DLRG was begun in 1913, approximately 5,000 people each year were drowning in Germany.

Prior to the formation of the DLRG an advisory central office for saving life on inland and coastal waters, located in Berlin, recommended that swimming be taught in public schools. In line with this, the DLRG adopted a motto from the Royal Life Saving Society—learn to swim, learn to save. Later, the DLRG slogan became—fight the wet death! Eight thousand people drowned in 1921 and in 1922 only 2-3 percent of all Germans were able to swim. It was obvious the DLRG had its work cut out for it. Between 1913-1943 over 1 million people were taught lifesaving and many were saved. This was accomplished by volunteers.

The DLRG desired unity and support from its members rather than competition with other clubs. By 1955 there were over 220,000 members of the DLRG. These members taught swimming and performed voluntary lifeguard services.

Recent Developments

1. Resuscitation
    Probably the most important relatively recent developments in lifesaving are in the area of resuscitation. In 1958, mouth to mouth resuscitation became the preferred method. Since 1966, mouth to mouth resuscitation has been joined with external cardiac compression to give those in lifesaving knowledge and techniques for saving lives that far surpasses the knowledge and technique of just thirty years ago.

    The American Red Cross teaches mouth to mouth resuscitation as part of its first aid and lifesaving courses. The CPR standards of the American Heart Association are followed in their development of community training for emergency cardiac care. Since heart arrest is often a subsequent condition in cases of drowning, the development of cardiopulmonary resuscitation, called CPR, has greatly increased lifesaving capabilities for lifeguards.

2. Equipment
    Significant progress in lifesaving equipment has evolved in recent years. Devices for mechanical resuscitation, inhalation, and aspiration are commonly used by rescue squads as well as being part of the equipment at many beaches and pools. Spine boards are now commonly used. The rescue tube, although dating back to about 1940, became popular in the early 1970s with career Red Cross people who promoted its use. Four wheel drive beach vehicles, power driven boats, and even helicopters have become part of the lifesaving equipment of various organizations. Communications have been improved by putting phones on lifeguard stands and by the use of two-way radios. Scuba equipment has added to the effectiveness of submerged body recovery and with a good pair of swim fins, lifesavers can move quickly through large surf to contact victims. Although the

eqiupment cited here certainly will not be available in many lifesaving situations, it has increased markedly lifesaving capabilities where it is available and used.

Changes in Recreational Swimming

Prior to and for most of the nineteenth century few people throughout the United States and Europe who went to the public baths or to the seashore resorts were swimmers. Most of these people were bathers—those who simply went to immerse themselves in the water and to perhaps jump up and down and play in the waves. It is an unfortunate fact that swimming is an accomplishment that has to be learned and, until the American Red Cross developed a nationwide program for teaching swimming there were few opportunities for people to learn how to swim in the United States. Private organizations, including the Y.M.C.A., had provided some opportunities for learning to swim before the Red Cross program, but these opportunities had been available to a limited number of people.

Although swimming was encouraged for men throughout the nineteenth century, women in America were expected to bathe. This attitude toward women began to change in the latter part of the century. Between 1890 to 1920 the social attitude turned around and women were encouraged to swim as well as to participate in other sports that had previously been considered unsuitable.

The change in the general social attitude toward women's right to swim is clearly shown in the style change of women's swimming costume. The bathing dress of the early nineteenth century became the trimmer bathing suit of the latter nineteenth century that gave way to the functional swimming suit of the early twentieth century.

The increase in swimming and its new popularity also brought about changes in lifesaving, particularly on the ocean beaches. During the nineteenth century when few people were swimmers, life lines would be extended into the water at one or more selected areas on a beach. These lines would be attached to poles. The bathers would congregate around these lines, holding onto them when the waves were a bit rough.

As more people started swimming, or at least attempted to swim with the little skill that they had, they moved away from the life lines and spread out on the beach. With changing public attitudes, brought about largely by a changing industrial society and urbanization, informal associations in public became more possible. However, this also encouraged a lack of formality and an adventurousness on the beach that hitherto had not been present. Consequently, by the 1920s most life lines had disappeared or fallen into disuse because more lifeguard stands were set up to guard the entire beach.

Presently, most people are still primarily bathers, although it is fashionable now to call oneself a swimmer even if all one does is immerse in the water like the nineteenth century bather. However, there is no doubt that more people actually do swim in this latter part of the century than at any time previously. Most people who are rescued today probably are not bathers, but are poor swimmers who have overextended themselves or have gotten themselves into a hazardous situation. Lifesavers, of course, have had to handle a greater variety of rescue problems under the changed situation. The various problems have been further increased over the years by the erection of jetties, groins, piers, and other types of shoreline construction.

A tremendous increase in the number of people who swim or bathe at some type of aquatic area or facility has occurred since the turn of the century. At the present, over half of all Americans go "swimming" for recreation. The increase in swimming has been accompanied by a rise in the number of available beaches and pools.

The increase in recreational swimming and the development of private or public aquatic facilities brought about accidents that ended up in court suits. Consequently, judicial decisions were made in the cases that came before the courts and these decisions resulted in a case law that set standards for the proprietors of the aquatic facilities.

The law suits that were considered came under two types of classifications. One classification was "dangerous or defective conditions." This dealt with problems arising from the condition of the facility or the water and beach area that was controlled by the proprietor in question. The other classification was "supervision and attendants." This dealt with problems arising from the presence or absence of supervision: lifeguards, their qualifications, their attentiveness, their responsiveness, their sufficient number, the presence of lifesaving equipment, and more.

Consequently, private proprietors or governments were encouraged by this to support standards in lifesaving, to make rules or regulations governing the use of their beaches and pools, and to expect a level of performance from their lifeguards that would prevent a plaintiff from successfully bringing suit. This pressure from the courts has substantially affected the success of the lifesaving movement in the United States.

6
Organization and Administration

Important Highlights:

1.	August,	1963	Lifeguard strike threatened —Long Beach, New York.
2.	July,	1964	Lifeguard strike—Wildwood Crest, New Jersey.
3.	July,	1965	Union representing lifeguards authorizes strike— Jones Beach, New York.
4.	July,	1966	Lifeguards walk off job— Coney Island.
5.	August,	1967	Forty lifeguards resign— North Wildwood, New Jersey.
6.	July,	1968	New York City beaches and pools hit by lifeguard strike.
7.	August,	1969	Lifeguards do not report for work—New Jersey and New York Palisades Interstate Park—swimming areas closed.
8.	August,	1970	Union representing lifeguards plans strike at Palisades Interstate Park.
9.	July,	1971	Union representing lifeguards at Jones Beach, Sunken

Meadows, and Robert Moses
State Parks ends strike—four
drown at Jones Beach during
strike, one at Robert Moses
State Park.

Organization and Administration

Organization involves the recognition of various activities that must be performed by a group of people, the assignment of these activities to identified positions, and the relationships that exist between the different positions. The performance of the assigned activities, particularly as this involves both a relationship between people in positions and a fulfillment of an organizational responsibility, is the main characteristic of administration.

Three types of positions are of interest when considering the organization and administration of a lifeguard operation:

1. Management positions
2. Supervisory lifeguards
3. Nonsupervisory lifeguards

Management positions primarily will be concerned with budget, salaries, hiring, firing, purchasing, planning, and development. Supervisory lifeguards will be concerned with maintaining the quality of lifeguard performance at a level of suitable standards through training, directing, correcting, evaluating, and reporting. Nonsupervisory lifeguards will be concerned with activities such as: rescuing, assisting, preventing accidents through directing, enforcing regulations, and maintaining a state of alertness and readiness to respond to emergency situations.

Management

The most common problem that people in management face, in regard to lifeguard protection, is a lack of understanding about the problems and needs of the operation. When management does not understand the problems and needs of the daily operation, an adversary relationship often develops between management and other positions. Management then may become reluctant to respond to normal lifeguard operational requests.

Lifeguards may in some cases respond to management's lack of leadership by resorting to inflated figures in terms of rescues or numbers of people served. Scare talk may be used in regard to currents or other hazards, in attempts to get results from management.

By turning off to the logical needs of a daily operation, or by ignoring trends in public use, management begins to take the position that something extraordinary must happen to "justify" any "needs." The result is crisis management. The strike is one aspect of crisis management. Drownings are another.

The history of lifeguarding and aquatic recreation have shown the need for available lifeguard protection. At the present over half of all Americans "swim" for recreation. "Swimming" is the third most popular outdoor recreational activity in the United States. Any knowledgeable person who goes to a few beaches and pools will see that the general quality of this "swimming" is not high.

Experienced lifeguards are aware of the personal risks most people take when they go "swimming." These lifeguards usually are aware of their responsibilities, the sensitivity of their performance which is constantly open to public scrutiny and criticism, and of the management support that is necessary for them adequately to fulfill their responsibilities. One of these support responsibilities is a "competitive" salary that will induce people who have the necessary skills to seek the lifeguard positions.

Another budget problem is for an adequate number of personnel to meet protection needs. Adequate supervision cannot be accomplished by the number of personnel minimally necessary to form a rescue squad. An effective lifeguard operation is not set up on the principle of responding to a call, as in the case of a rescue squad. Hiring a rescue squad and calling it a lifeguard operation does not make it one, although it can certainly reduce the budget considerably.

Other areas of budget concern and lifeguard support needs are: rescue equipment, stands, chairs or towers, a communications system, a records system, first aid supplies and equipment, training aids such as resuscitation manikins, training time and course attendance opportunities, binoculars and other pertinent items or materials, and a well planned posting of regulations for the visitor. Also needed is the availability of safety information through pamphlets, displays, and lifeguard talks and demonstrations. Reports from supervisory lifeguards should be thoroughly reviewed and analysed for all management submissions of the budget. The manager who ignores reports from

A 1928 photograph shows lifeguard stands and surf boats at Atlantic City, New Jersey near the shoreline. To the right of the nearest boat is a torpedo buoy set up on a box that holds a line (Photograph courtesy of Library of Congress).

supervisory lifeguards is not meeting the responsibilities that are expected of one in that position. Such managers may pay a heavy price later for ignoring present situations.

Mutual respect and cooperation between the people in management positions and those in the nonmanagement positions are indispensable for an effective, efficient, and harmonious operation. For managers the achievement of this respect and cooperation should be a challenge because so many managers of recreation areas with beaches or pools do not have a good background in aquatics and water safety. However, by using the facility like a visitor, by asking questions, and by finding out what basically is going on, the needs for support in the field will become more apparent. The managers can then use their administrative knowledge and experience to lead the field staff in fulfilling the basic principles of a lifeguard operation. Needed major services will then be more likely to be delivered where and when they are needed.

Supervisory Lifeguards

The supervisory lifeguards should conduct prejob training for all lifeguards. This training should be a minimum of two days for any facility or area, and might last a week if the organization can afford to put the lifeguards on soon enough. Any training should include the following: CPR, livesaving skills, first aid, rescue equipment, legal responsibilities, enforcement procedures, hazards of the area or facility, and organization and administration of the operation.

A program of daily in-service training and workouts should be mandatory throughout the period of employment. Excellent physical condition and proficiency in use of equipment or related necessary job skills should be maintained. Any operation that can allow lifeguards to take a lunch break during the middle of the day can allow some lifeguards to workout while others are on stand duty, particularly early in the morning. Supervisors should be responsible for seeing that the in-service training meets established standards.

When necessary activities involve communication and cooperation among lifeguards, the supervisory lifeguard should be responsible to see that everyone involved knows what to do and does it properly. In situations where large numbers of people are affected in regard to beach use, or in emergency situations where experience is valuable, the supervisory lifeguard should direct the other lifeguards as needed. The supervisory lifeguard is responsible for the total safety and control of the protected area under his or her care.

Besides directing nonsupervisory lifeguards when needed, the supervisory lifeguard should correct them when necessary. Sometimes lifeguards do not follow the directions as they were intended. Problems while making enforcements often arise and judgment errors in making rescues may occur. A lifeguard may arrive late for work, stay too long for lunch, not adequately observe the people in the water, slack off in workouts, and more. All of these situations require detection and correction by the supervisor.

Supervisors should set good example as well as correct the mistakes of others. It is this quality that gives validity to the supervisor's task of evaluating the lifeguards under his or her supervision. A job evaluation should be completed at the end of the year or season. This record should be in writing and it should evaluate important elements such as the lifeguard's initiative, acceptance of supervision, dependability, and skill on the job.

The supervisory lifeguard should be responsible for reporting the condition of equipment. All equipment should be maintained properly by keeping it clean, and repairing damages such as dings in boards or frayed ropes. Also, the supervisor should make sure that rescue equipment is accessible, being placed where it can be quickly and readily used.

Other reports the supervisor should be responsible for collecting and maintaining are those that deal with daily conditions such as the water and weather, attendance and activities at the beach or pool. Reports should also be made for rescues and first aid. A comprehensive annual report should be turned in to management at the end of the year or season.

Facility and area maintenance are also of concern to the supervisory lifeguard. Cleanliness and health should be maintained, and any supervisor who sees unsanitary conditions should take steps to correct the situation, or report the condition to someone responsible for correction. Any dangerous or defective conditions, such as a log coming into the surf zone or a protruding nail on a boardwalk, require removal, correction, or in the absence of these, acts of prevention and warning. Lifeguards are often on the spot where dangerous or defective conditions exist. The supervisory lifeguard should take corrective action if a nonsupervisory lifeguard does not quickly and properly handle such a situation.

Supervisory lifeguards must be prepared to report to and communicate with management if optimum efficiency and effectiveness is to be achieved in the field. There is no substitute for what people can do if they work together with mutual respect and cooperation. Often this respect and cooperation must be earned by both sides. Management needs factual data and information and an accurate portrayal of conditions they cannot observe on a daily basis as the lifeguards can. The supervisory lifeguard can supply this data and information and provide a basis for an improved organizational relationship and greater administrative support and efficiency.

Nonsupervisory Lifeguards

Every lifeguard wants to avoid the accusation of being negligent. A lifeguard's negligence can cost a person his or her life. Negligence has been defined as substandard care (*Corpus Juris Secundum. Volume 65*).

Swimming is recognized as a hazardous recreation and consequently, anyone who goes swimming assumes some amount of personal risk. Nevertheless, inattention by a lifeguard can mean the difference between a life saved and a life lost. Lack of concern by a lifeguard can mean the difference between an injury avoided and an injury received.

The lifeguard who wants to be valued in a good operation will show initiative. Many things have to be done during the day besides sitting on the stand, whether it is picking up some trash, taking the water temperature, sweeping out the office, or putting out some of the heavier equipment, such as rescueboards. The person who shows initiative sees that something has to be done, realizes that it would not be improper for she or he to do it under the circumstances, and goes ahead and does it without waiting to be told. People who show initiative save time and time is valuable.

A lifeguard who accepts supervision creates a smoother working operation. There are many ways not to accept supervision. Moving slowly and reluctantly after a directive, acting contrary to a directive, arguing, and bad-mouthing behind the supervisor's back are ways of not accepting supervision. To accept supervision does not mean that a lifeguard does not express a different opinion. But the opinion should be based on substance, and not simply a tactic for avoiding cooperation.

Dependability is one of the most valuable attributes a lifeguard can possess. Without it, a lifeguard may be more trouble than help. The lifeguard who shows a lack of attention or skill or tends to be slow in reaction cannot be considered dependable. Other lifeguards who are dependable will become concerned about the area in front of the lifeguard who is not dependable. Working relationships will become strained. The supervisory lifeguard will probably recommend dismissal of an undependable lifeguard if there is sufficient cause to convincingly show the lack of dependability.

Skill on the job is measured by many variables. One of the most important skills is visual perception—the ability to analyze and understand visually what one is viewing. Closely allied to visual perception is the ability to concentrate. The ability to handle people satisfactorily in enforcement, rescue, or first aid situations is important. A lifeguard who can analyze the environment and the people, and be able to anticipate and perhaps prevent problems, has a valuable skill. In a general sense, it is a compliment to any lifeguard to have her or his co-workers believe that the lifeguard uses good judgment. In this discussion of job skills, it is assumed that all lifeguards have the necessary physical skills to do the job. After all, preservice and in-service training should mold all lifeguards into highly capable rescuers.

Summary of Operational Management Systems

In fulfilling the functions of the basic principles of lifeguarding by supervising, controlling, and rescuing, lifeguards establish a situation in which important data in regard to activities of the users, conditions of the area, and services rendered by the lifeguards may be collected. This data should be contained in a record system. The records should be summarized and analyzed,

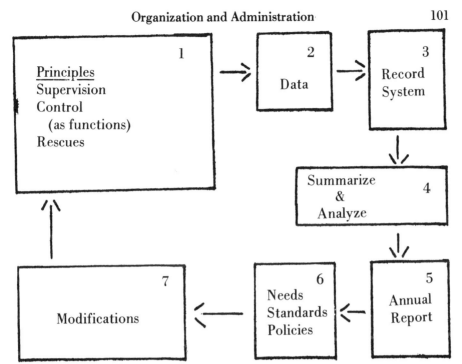

and should constitute the basis of an annual report. Also this report should include commentary on needs, standards, and policies, based on the data. These needs, standards, and policies as stated in the annual report should either support existing needs, standards, and policies, or indicate modifications. If modifications are indicated, then these changes will in turn affect the operation and should bring about greater efficiency and effectiveness. This system answers many of the administrative questions already indicated in this section, as well as those questions concerning manpower utilization and scheduling.

In summary, it may be noted that the days of "Bustem and Rollem" are long gone, and the days of the competent professional are looming on the horizon. We are past the time when communities were satisfied with the placement of a danger sign on the beach and the installation of poles with life lines on them in the water. The time when the public was satisfied to have lifeguards working as waiters and serving beer and hot dogs between rescues is over. We are past the time when the lifeguard with "savvy" knew the best way to deliver a knockout punch in the water, and carried a flask of whiskey on his hip to revive those victims he did not decide to roll over a barrel. And too, we are past the time when lifeguards who lack knowledge of the principles of lifeguarding can manage successfully the beaches and pools that are used heavily by our modern, recreation oriented and litigation minded public. Above all we know that the trends in recreation, generally, and aquatics in particular, have indicated the need for professional lifeguard services along the clear lines of simple principles, to which lifeguards can be committed as well as held accountable.

Glossary

ASSIST—An assist occurs when a person in the water is given aid but it was likely that the person could have gotten to safety on his or her own efforts

BACKWASH CURRENT—A backwash current is the gravitational, seaward flow of water down a beach face after a wave has broken and sent water up the beach face above the general water level in the ocean. A backwash current, to significantly affect people, usually must occur on a slope of 6° or more

BEACH—In geographical terms a beach is a collection of loose materials, such as sand, subject to normal wave action. Consequently, the near-shore sandy section that is affected by waves is technically part of the beach. That part of the beach that is relatively flat and usually dry we often think of as "the beach," but technically it is only that part of the beach known as the "berm"

DISTRESS—When a person in the water is not drowning but cannot reach safety without aid this situation constitutes distress

EMERGENCY—An urgent and unforeseen situation that requires immediate action is an emergency. In a professional lifeguard operation, the training, functions, and activities that constitute an effective response to an emergency are primarily integrated into routine operational characteristics. Consequently, the significant characteristic of an emergency response, beyond daily operational functions, is the availability of an outside telephone or radio for calling a unit that can bring a victim into an emergency treatment system in the community, or for calling an outside source for expert information or advice

HAZARD—A hazard is an environmental situation that constitutes a threat to safety

103

LITTORAL CURRENT—A littoral current runs parallel to the shoreline

OFFSET CURRENT—An offset current runs away from the shoreline at less than 90°

OFFSHORE CURRENT—An offshore current runs away from the shoreline, further than backwash, and perpendicular to the shoreline. However, it does not go through a sandbar outside its origin

PULL—Lower mid-Atlantic states jargon; "a pull" means a rescue, and derives from the towing of the victim to shore with a torpedo buoy

RESCUE—A rescue occurs when a person in the water is given aid, any aid, so that the person gets to safety, and it was not likely that the person could have gotten to safety on his or her own efforts

RIP CURRENT—A rip current topographically cuts or "rips" a channel through sand deposits (a sandbar) and moves seaward, perpendicular to the shoreline

SEA PUSS—This is an old term that is often misunderstood but it refers to a cyclical whirling of water at the juncture of two currents that possibly occurs when the head (outside part) of a rip current meets an outside set or littoral flow caused by the general wave approach

Selected Bibliography

Current Lifesaving Texts

Deutsche Lebens-Rettungs-Gesellschaft. *Die Befreiungsgriffe der DLRG.* Duisburg-Ruhrort: Deutsche Lebens-Rettungs-Gesellschaft, 1955.

Deutsche Lebens-Rettungs-Gesellschaft. *Wiederbelebung und Erste Hilfe.* 43 Essen: Deutsche Lebens-Rettungs-Gesellschaft, n.d.

Silvia, Charles E. *Lifesaving and Water Safety Today.* New York: Association Press, 1968.

The American National Red Cross. *Lifesaving: Rescue and Water Safety.* New York: Doubleday & Company, Inc., 1974.

The Royal Life Saving Society. *Life Saving and Water Safety.* London: The Royal Life Saving Society, United Kingdom, 1973.

The Surf Life Saving Association of Australia. *Handbook of Instruction and Examination.* Sydney: The Surf Life Saving Association of Australia, 1964.

Historical Aspects of Lifesaving, Lifeguarding, Bathing and Swimming

Allen, Lane, and Scott. *The Sea-side Resorts of New Jersey.* Philadelphia: Allen, Lane, and Scott, 1877.

Andrews, W. D. *Swimming and Life-Saving.* Toronto: William Briggs, 1889.

Australia, Waverly Municipal Council. *Waverly Municipality 1859-1959.* Sydney: Waverly Municipal Council, n.d.

Casson, Lionel. *Daily Life In Ancient Rome.* New York: American Heritage Publishing Co., Inc., 1975.

Contini, Mila. *Fashion From Ancient Egypt to the Present Day.* New York: Crescent Books, 1965.

Delgado, Alan. *Victorian Entertainment.* New York: American Heritage Press, 1971.

Dulles, Rhea Foster. *A History of Recreation: America Learns to Play.* New York: Appleton-Century-Crofts, 1965.

Durst, Elain Autumn. "The Functional Aspect of One Type of Women's Sportswear from 1900-1958 in the United States." Master's thesis, Michigan State University, 1959.

English, A. L. *History of Atlantic City New Jersey.* Philadelphia: Dickson & Gilling, 1884.

Funnell, Charles E. *By the Beautiful Sea.* New York: Alfred A. Knopf, 1975.

Gaunt, Arthur. "150 Years of Sea Rescue." *Sea Frontiers* 21: 21-28.

Goss, George E. *Life Saving.* New York: Association Press, 1916.

Handley, L. De. B. *Swimming and Watermanship.* New York: The Macmillan Company, 1922.

Ingersoll, Luther A. *Ingersoll's Century History—Santa Monica Bay Cities.* Los Angeles: Luther A. Ingersoll, 1908.

Kidwell, Claudia B. *Women's Bathing and Swimming Costume in the United States.* Washington, D.C.: U.S. Government Printing Office, 1969.

Kybalova, Ludmila, Herbenova, Olga, and Lamarova, Milena. *The Pictorial Encyclopedia of Fashion.* New York: Paul Hamlyn, 1970.

Lohr, Karl. *Lernt Schwimmen und Retten.* Schorndorf, Germany: Karl Hofmann, 1968.

Manning-Sanders, Ruth. *Seaside England.* London: B. T. Batsford, LTD., 1951.

Margan, Frank., and Finney, Ben R. *A Pictorial History of Surfing.* Sydney: Paul Hamlyn, 1970.

Mee, Charles L. *Daily Life in Renaissance Italy.* New York: American Heritage Publishing Co., Inc., 1975.

Pilot, Oliver Ramsay. *Sodom by the Sea.* New York: Doubleday & Co., Inc., 1941.

Rainwater, Clarence E. *The Play Movement in the United States, A Study of Community Recreation.* Washington, D.C.: McGrath Publishing Company, (n.d. originally published 1922).

Scott, George Ryley. *The Story of Baths and Bathing.* London: T. Werner Laurie LTD., 1939.

Sicklemore, R. *History of Brighton And Its Environs.* Brighton: C. and R. Sicklemore, 1827.

Sinclair, Archibald, and Henry, William. *Swimming.* Boston: Little, Brown, and Co., 1893.

Special Park Commission, City Council of Chicago. *Public Bathing Beaches,* 1913.

United States Bureau of Outdoor Recreation. 1973. *Outdoor Recreation A Legacy for America.*

United States Outdoor Recreation Resources Review Commission. 1962. *Outdoor Recreation for America.*

United States Senate. 1974. *The Recreation Imperative.* Committee On Interior And Insular Affairs.

United States Volunteer Life Saving Corps. *Annual Reports.*

Walton, Frank E. *The Sea Is My Work Shop*. New York: E. P. Dutton & Company, 1935.

Winston, Clara, and Winston, Richard. *Daily Life In The Middle Ages*. New York: American Heritage Publishing Company, Inc., 1975.

Legal Aspects of Lifeguarding

Debevec, Robert M. *Laws Governing Amusements*. New York: Oceana Publications, Inc., 1960.

Dyer, Donald B., and Lichtig, J. G. *Liability in Public Recreation*. Appleton, Wisconsin: C. C. Nelsen Publishing Company, 1949.

Shearman, Thomas G., and Redfield, Amasa A. *A Treatise on the Law of Negligence Revised Edition Volume Four*. New York: Baker, Voorhis & Company, Inc., 1941.

The Publishers Editorial Staff. *Negligence Compensation Cases Annotated Volume Three*. Chicago: Callaghan and Company, 1938.

The Publishers Editorial Staff. *Negligence Compensation Cases Annotated 4th Series Volume 3*. Chicago: Callaghan and Company, 1969.

Organization and Administration

Baker, Richard D. "Records Use: A Necessity for Administration of Protected Beach Operations" *Guideline*. Dec. 1970.

Beck, Arthur C., ed., and Hillmar, Ellis D., ed. *A Practical Approach to Organization Development Through MBO—Selected Readings*. Reading, Massachusetts: Addison-Wesley Publishing Company, 1972.

Etzioni, Amitari. *Modern Organizations*. New Jersey: Prentice-Hall, Inc., 1964.

Sherman, Harvey. *It All Depends*. University, Alabama: University of Alabama Press, 1970.

The Physical Beach Environment

Baker, Richard D. "Dangerous Shore Currents." *Sea Frontiers* 18: 138-143.

Bascom, Willard. *Waves and Beaches*. New York: Doubleday & Company, Inc., 1964.

Bird, E. C. F. *Coasts*. Cambridge: The Massachusetts Institute of Technology Press, 1968.

Defant, Albert. *Ebb and Flow*. Ann Arbor: The University of Michigan Press, 1964.

King, Cuchlaine A. M. *Beaches and Coasts*. London: Edward Arnold, 1961.

Minikin, R. R. *Winds, Waves and Maritime Structures*. London: Griffin, 1963.

Russell, Richard J. *River Plains and Sea Coasts*. Berkeley: University of California Press, 1967.

Shephard, Frances P. *Submarine Geology*. New York: Harper & Row, 1963.

Shephard, France P., and Wanless, Harold R. *Our Changing Coastlines*. New York: McGraw-Hill Book Company, 1971.

Tricker, R. A. R. *Bores, Breakers, Waves and Wakes*. New York: American Elsevier Publishing Company, Inc., 1964.

United States Navy. *Wind Waves at Sea Breakers and Surf*. Washington, D.C.: Hydrographic Office, 1952.

Appendix

In doing research for this book, the author found interesting historical materials at the following institutions:

1. Library of Congress, Division of Photographs and Prints
2. National Archives, Ford Film Collection
3. National Gallery of Art

Research materials in the Longfellow Historical Archives of the American National Red Cross consisted mainly of reports, official letters, notes, and copies of talks, pageants, etc.

Footnoting this book would have lead to tedious reading. Enough information on sources has been given to enable the reader who is interested to quickly begin his or her own investigations.

Index